S0-BXV-457

STAR WARS ™

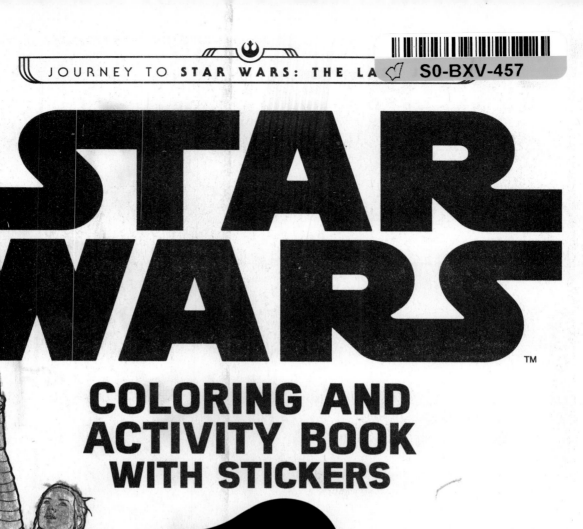

COLORING AND ACTIVITY BOOK
WITH STICKERS

starwars.com

© & ™ Lucasfilm Ltd.

IMPOSTER

Find the C-3PO that is different, that's the real C-3PO.

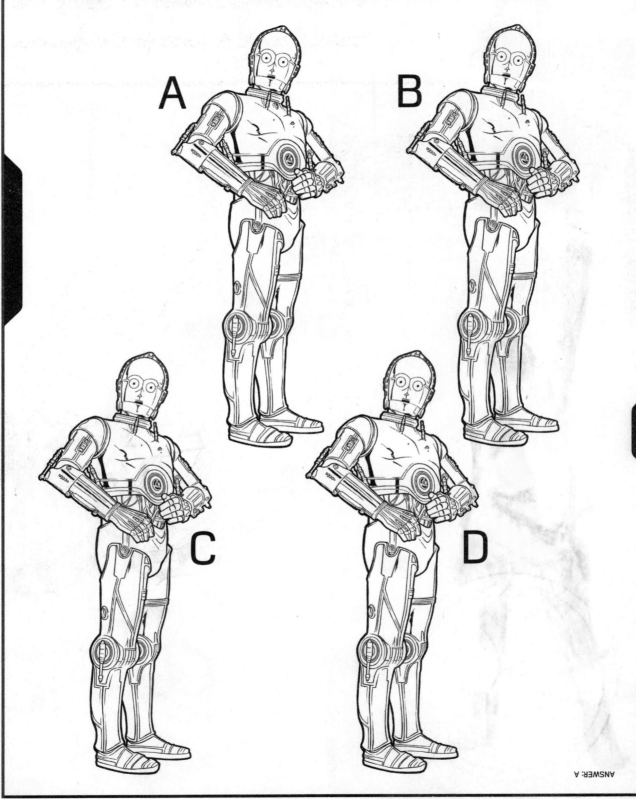

ANSWER: A

REY and **CHEWBACCA** pilot a Corellian light freighter called the **MILLENNIUM FALCON**. The **FALCON** is known for being the fastest hunk of junk in the galaxy.

SQUARES

Taking turns, connect a line from one symbol to another. Whoever makes the line that completes the box puts their initials inside that box. The person with the most squares at the end of the game wins!

Example

TIC-TAC-TOE

Challenge a friend to a game of tic-tac-toe.

On Ahch-To, **REY** seeks out the great Jedi Master **LUKE SKYWALKER. LUKE** is the last hope for the Resistance.

MISSING PIECE

Find the square that completes the picture.

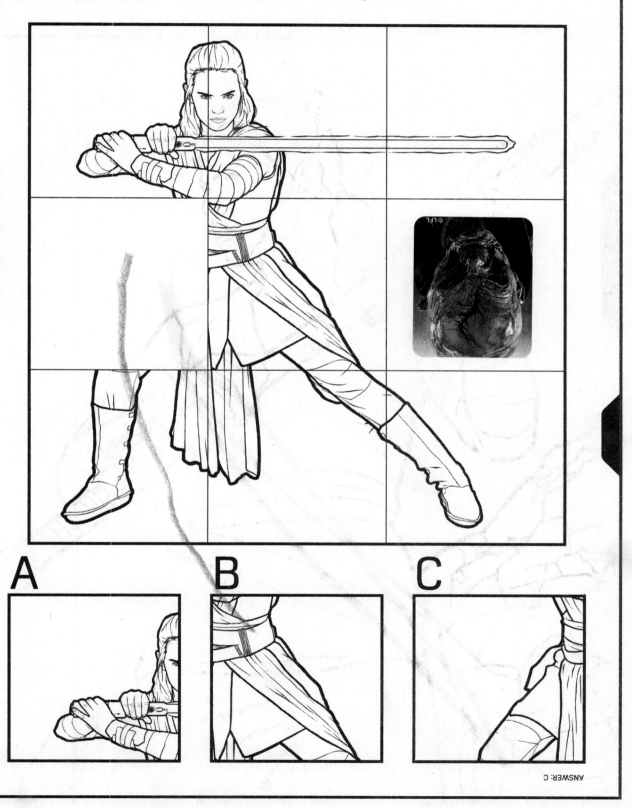

A

B

C

SECRET CODE

Using the secret code decipher the message.

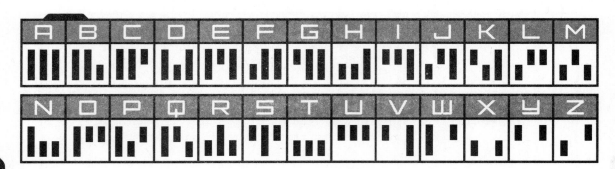

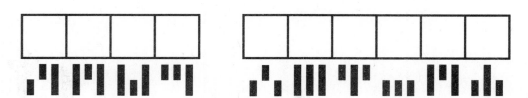

DESIGN PAGE

Design your own Resistance Starfighter.

REY hopes to learn the ways of the

Force from **LUKE SKYWALKER.**

SECTOR GRID

Use the grid to help you draw the picture.

Rey

LUKE SKYWALKER retreated to Ahch-To after his attempt to rebuild the Jedi Knights was thwarted by the dark side of the Force. Now the Resistance needs his help to stop the evil First Order.

WORD SEARCH

Find the words listed in the puzzle below.

AWING   MILLENNIUM
RESISTANCE   FORCE
SKYWALKER   FALCON
CHEWBACCA   XWING

```
S K Y W A L K E R H H
R U P U Q I T Z X Y X
C H E W B A C C A X W
A S E C J A Q G N V I
S F O R C E W R T R N
M I L L E N N I U M G
W Z M F C S W R N J H
Z R E I G W U I D G R
E F A L C O N I T Z G
B E C N A T S I S E R
M O E N Y Z X H P Z G
```

© LFL

TRACER

Use the lines to help you draw Luke Skywalker.

LUKE SKYWALKER lives in peace with the other inhabitants of the island. **CARETAKERS** look after the ancient Jedi structures.

© LFL

HOW MANY WORDS

See how many words you can make from the letters in:

JEDI MASTER

TIC-TAC-TOE

Challenge a friend to a game of tic-tac-toe.

For years, **LUKE SKYWALKER** has lived on a remote island on the planet Ahch-To. **LUKE** lives off of the land and keeps to himself.

SQUARES

Taking turns, connect a line from one symbol to another. Whoever makes the line that completes the box puts their initials inside that box. The person with the most squares at the end of the game wins!

Example

IMPOSTER

The First Order has incerted spy astromech units into the Resistance. The real BB-8 is the one that is different.

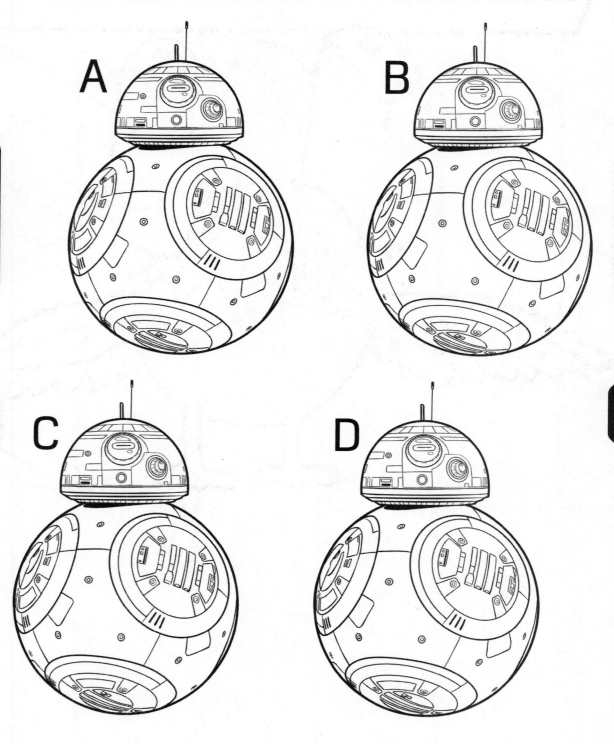

Small, flat-muzzled curious creatures called **PORGS** flock among the rocks and roost in the cliffs of **LUKE'S** island home.

With the power of the Force awakening inside her,
REY prepares to travel to the hidden world of
Ahch-To, along with her faithful Wookiee
co-pilot and first mate, **CHEWBACCA.**

Now that **REY** has found **LUKE SKYWALKER**, the last Jedi Master in the galaxy. But **LUKE** challenges **REY'S** expectations.

SECTOR GRID

Use the grid to help you draw the picture.

C-3PO

DESIGN PAGE

Design your own Astromech droid.

WORD SEARCH

Find the words listed in the puzzle below.

SKYWALKER   **REY**
CHEWBACCA   **FINN**
MILLENNIUM   **POE**
FALCON   **DAMERON**

```
F  S  K  Y  W  A  L  K  E  R  V
I  C  H  E  W  B  A  C  C  A  S
N  J  S  P  H  R  E  Y  Z  G  F
N  H  B  D  W  J  O  E  R  V  B
S  L  Y  Y  D  A  M  E  R  O  N
M  I  L  L  E  N  N  I  U  M  L
X  E  S  G  P  D  G  L  M  J  X
J  Q  J  H  A  O  I  H  B  P  W
O  Z  A  B  G  C  E  G  V  W  I
C  W  C  G  G  S  P  J  B  R  N
X  B  E  F  A  L  C  O  N  W  G
```

SECRET CODE

Using the secret code decipher the message.

TRACER

Use the lines to help you draw Finn.

Former stormtrooper **FINN** has healed from the injuries inflicted by **KYLO REN'S** lightsaber. Now a part of the Resistance ranks, **FINN** has little time to celebrate the destruction of the First Order's deadly Starkiller super weapon or wonder what has become of his friend **REY.**

© LFL

MISSING PIECE

Find the square that completes the picture.

A

B

C

TIC-TAC-TOE

Challenge a friend to a game of tic-tac-toe.

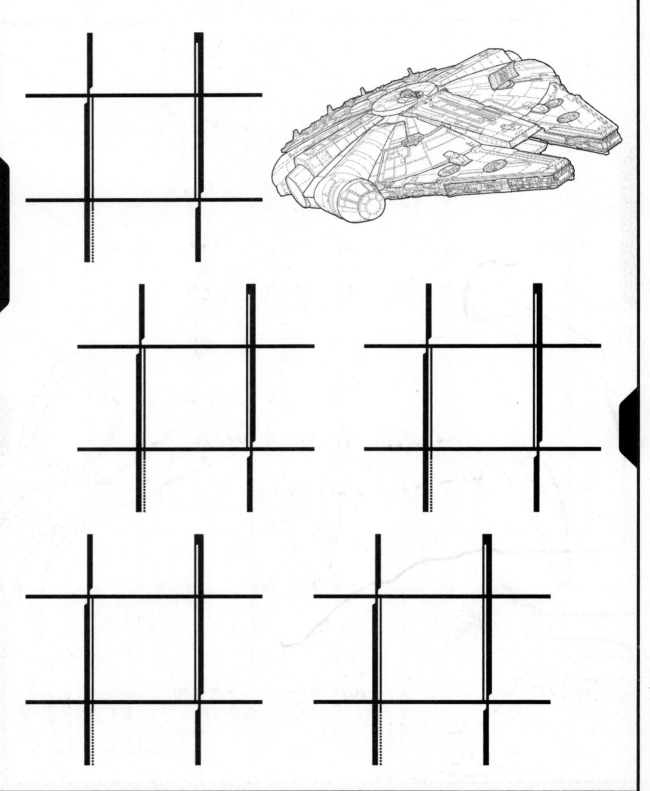

While **REY** and **LUKE** explore matters of the Force, **CHEWBACCA** gets to know the wildlife and inhabitants of the remote island.

SQUARES

Taking turns, connect a line from one symbol to another. Whoever makes the line that completes the box puts their initials inside that box. The person with the most squares at the end of the game wins!

Example

TRACER

Use the lines to help you draw Poe Dameron.

The threat of the First Order is of great concern to the ever-worried protocol droid **C-3PO**. He continues to serve **GENERAL LEIA ORGANA** on the bridge of the Resistance cruiser.

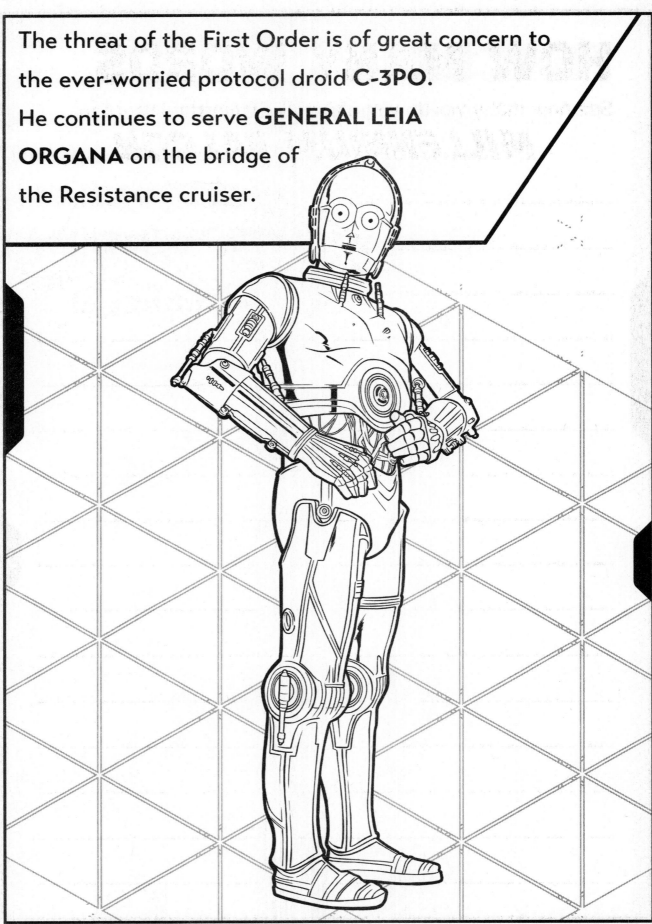

HOW MANY WORDS

See how many words you can make from the letters in:

MILLENNIUM FALCON

_____

_____

_____

_____   _____

_____   _____

_____   _____

_____   _____

_____   _____

_____   _____

_____   _____

_____   _____

_____   _____

IMPOSTER

Find the Resistance pilot that is different, that is the imposter pilot.

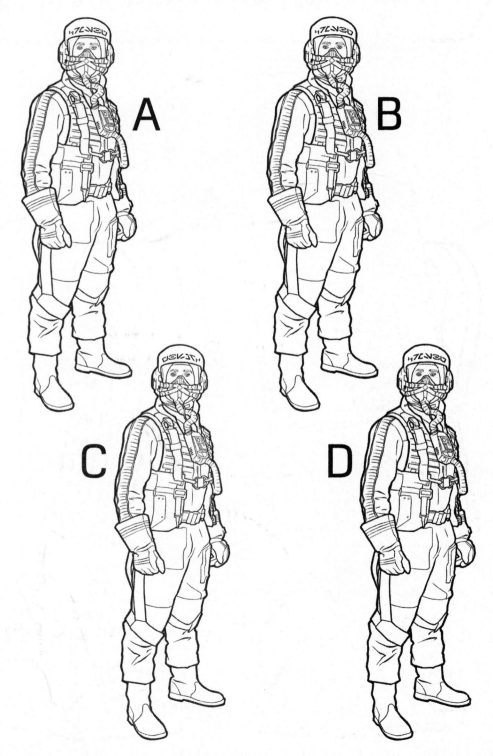

A

B

C

D

© LFL

LUKE SKYWALKER'S faithful astromech droid remained dormant for years after his master disappeared. Now reactivated, **R2-D2** travels with **REY** and **CHEWBACCA** to Ahch-To.

DESIGN PAGE

Design your own lightsaber.

SECTOR GRID

Use the grid to help you draw the picture.

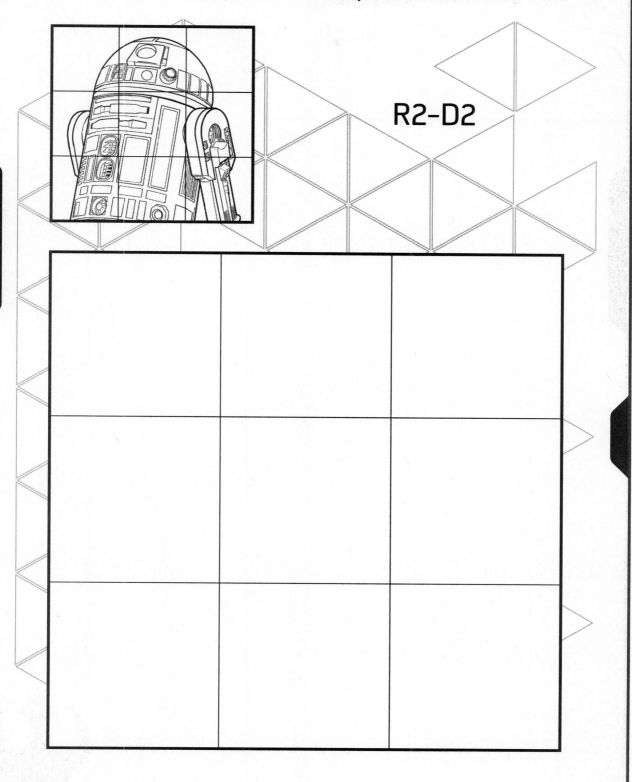

R2-D2

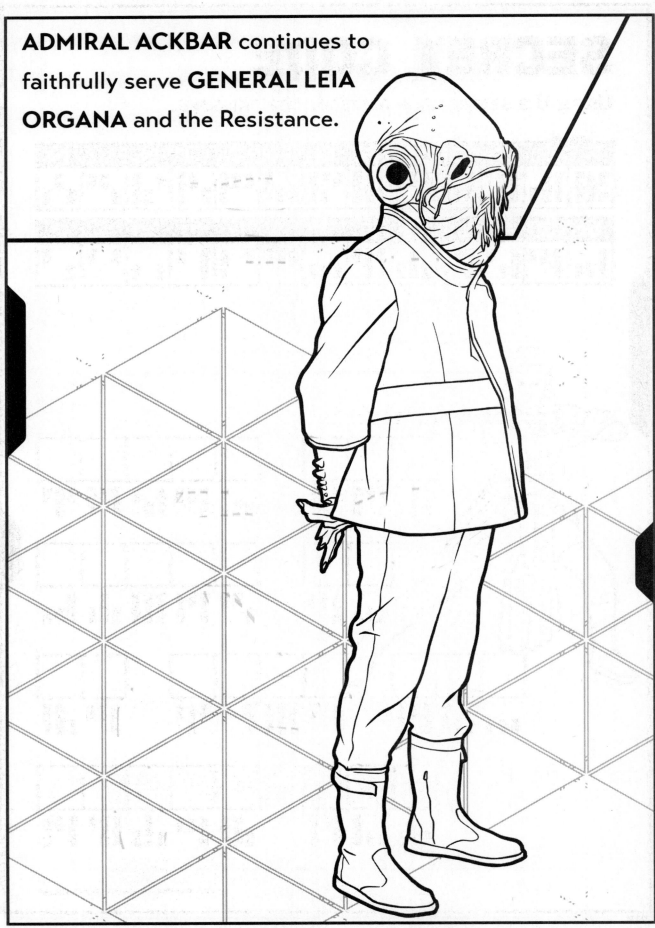

ADMIRAL ACKBAR continues to faithfully serve **GENERAL LEIA ORGANA** and the Resistance.

SECRET CODE

Using the secret code decipher the message.

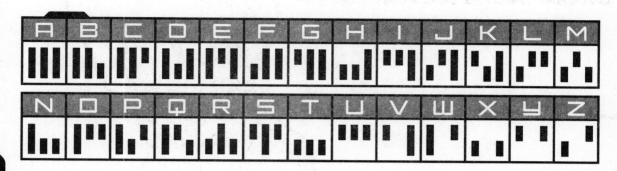

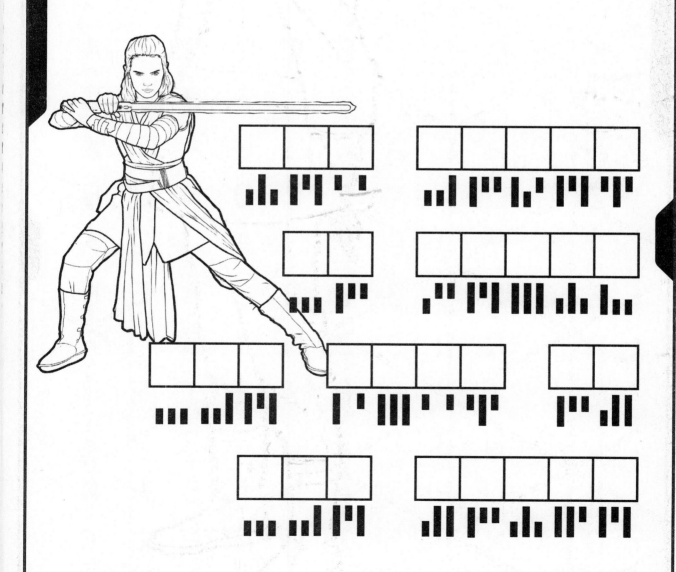

ANSWER: Rey hopes to learn the ways of the Force.

WORD SEARCH

Find the words listed in the puzzle below.

DAMERON	ACKBAR
PORGS	GENERAL
LEIA	ORGANA
C3PO	R2D2

```
K X Q S P O R G S O A
Z R E R 2 D 2 F P 2 C
W 2 H D A S G H A P K
Z E D A M E R O N J B
2 G Y J G L J A H G A
Z G Z C Z E C O A E R
H F R Q 3 3 N I S M F
M L T Y R P Z E I E B
L E U 3 C 3 O I R R 2
X I O R G A N A S A K
O A N V H T W C H L L
```

Once again on the run from dark forces determined to crush freedom in the galaxy, **LEIA ORGANA** leads the Resistance fleet on its quest to find allies across the galaxy.

SQUARES

Taking turns, connect a line from one symbol to another. Whoever makes the line that completes the box puts their initials inside that box. The person with the most squares at the end of the game wins!

Example

MISSING PIECE

Find the square that completes the picture.

A

B

C

Part of the support crew that keeps the Resistance starfighters flying, **ROSE** has hated the First Order since she was a child. Now able to fight back against the enemy, **ROSE** keeps her focus on her mission.

© LFL

TRACER

Use the lines to help you draw Rey.

TIC-TAC-TOE

Challenge a friend to a game of tic-tac-toe.

HOW MANY WORDS

See how many words you can make from the letters in:

GENERAL LEIA ORGANA

DESIGN PAGE

Design a Jedi Knight.

IMPOSTER

Find the real Poe Dameron, those that are different are the imposters.

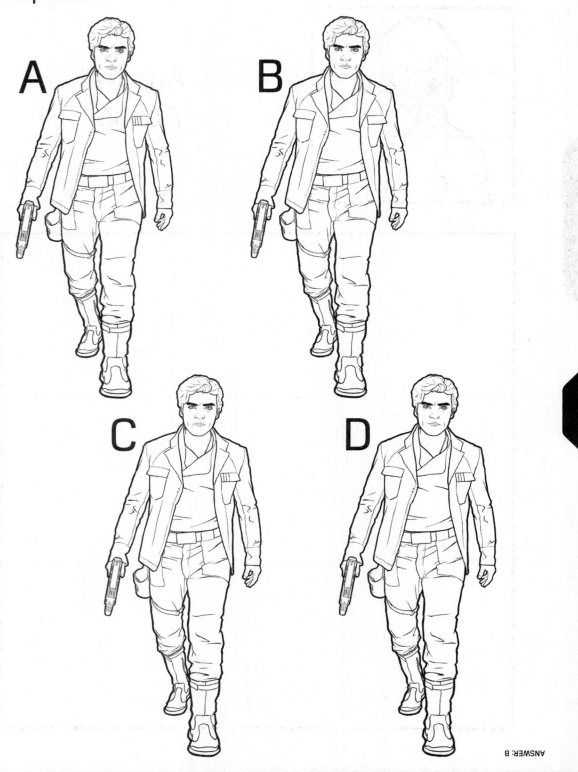

A

B

C

D

SECTOR GRID

Use the grid to help you draw the picture.

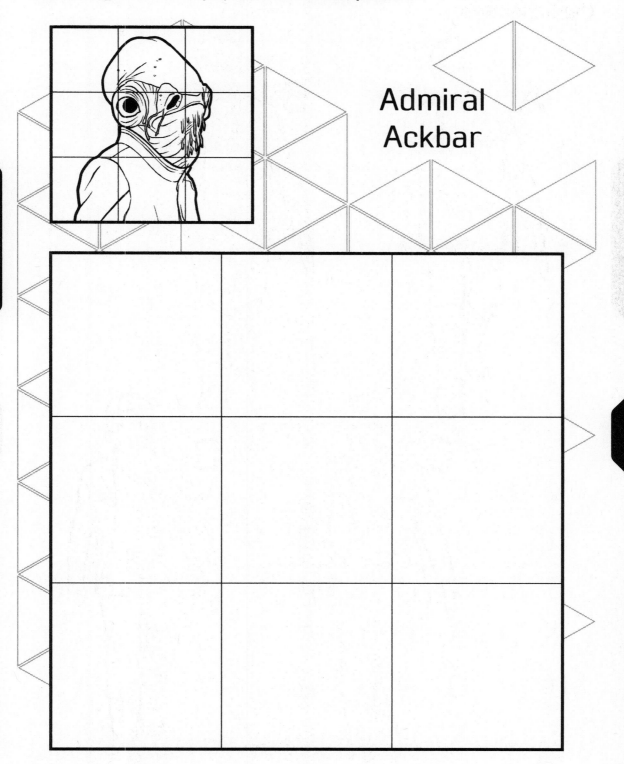

Admiral
Ackbar

WORD SEARCH

Find the words listed in the puzzle below.

JEDI	KNIGHT
BB8	ASTROMECH
MASTER	FORCE
GALAXY	RESISTANCE

```
H R S M C H A V Q Q X
Q R E S I S T A N C E
H C E M O R T S A G I
X P A S N M T V B H D
F S T A A F H U W N E
N E O S V K O V K B J
Q I T G S D N R B S Z
E E T J L H E I C Q O
R Q 8 B B E D O G E O
U P G A L A X Y E H Z
J S K O C O Z I T K T
```

TRACER

Use the lines to help you draw C-3PO.

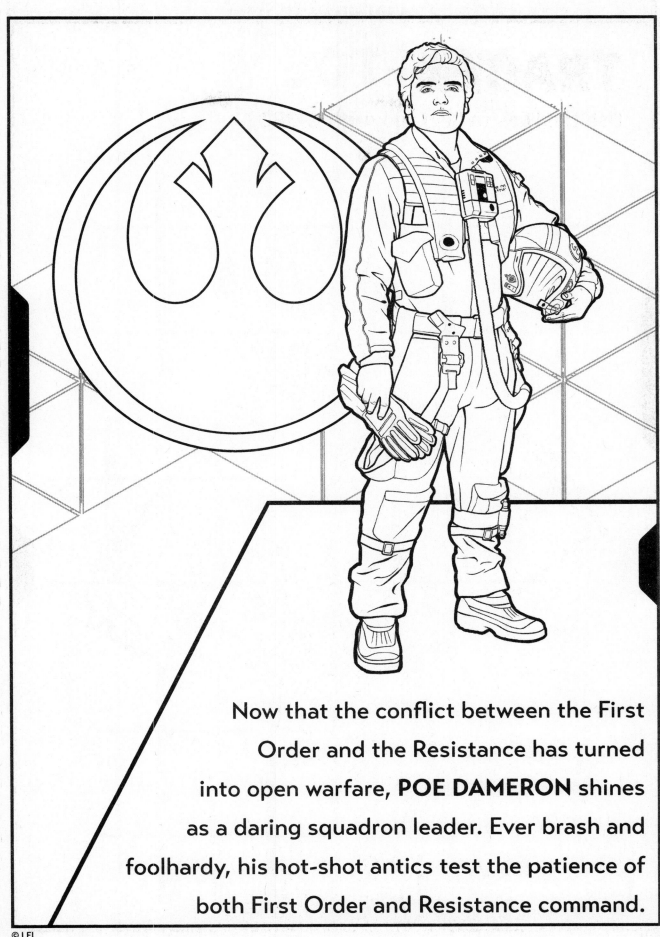

Now that the conflict between the First Order and the Resistance has turned into open warfare, **POE DAMERON** shines as a daring squadron leader. Ever brash and foolhardy, his hot-shot antics test the patience of both First Order and Resistance command.

TIC-TAC-TOE

Challenge a friend to a game of tic-tac-toe.

It takes a defiant courage to stare down the threat of the First Order, and while **CAPTAIN POE DAMERON** is eager to fight, he worries that some in the Resistance leadership do not have what it takes.

Brave and loyal **BB-8** continues his service to **POE DAMERON** but also is a good friend and resourceful ally to **FINN** and **ROSE**.

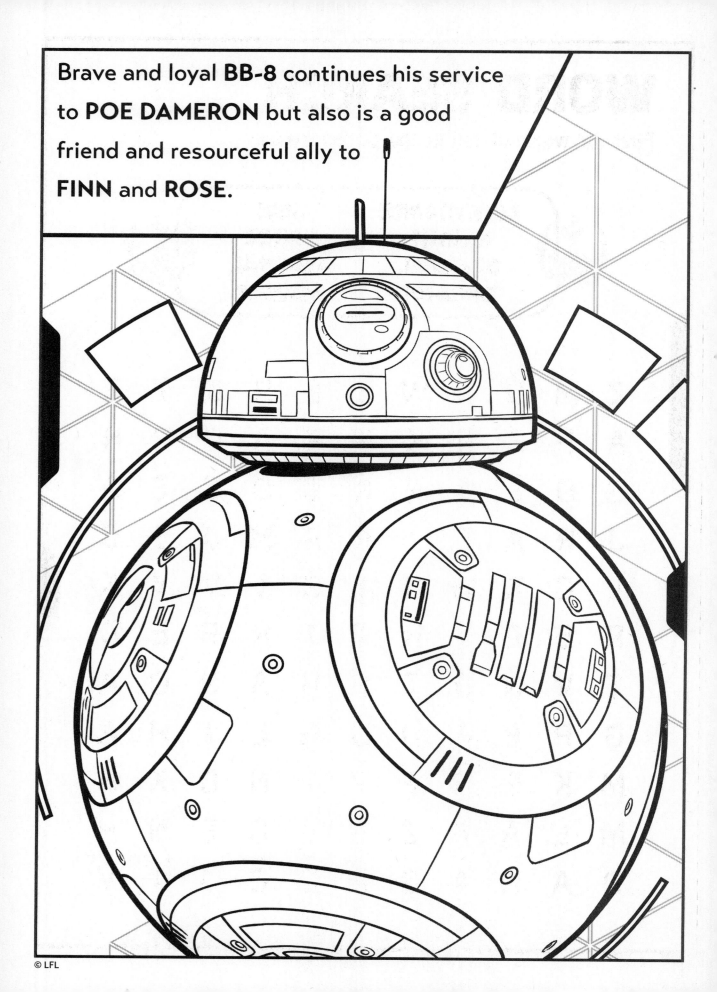

WORD SEARCH

Find the words listed in the puzzle below.

LIGHTSABRE	JEDI
KNIGHT	FORCE
GENERAL	ADMIRAL
ORGANA	ACKBAR

```
Z  M  U  X  W  Z  E  R  K  T  Z
A  F  Z  R  K  N  R  A  D  P  R
S  O  L  A  N  K  B  D  C  Z  A
J  R  A  E  I  R  A  M  J  S  B
L  C  R  W  G  I  S  I  V  Y  K
R  E  E  I  H  T  T  R  F  E  C
T  V  N  J  T  F  H  A  N  O  A
G  P  E  W  H  U  G  L  I  H  A
M  K  G  J  E  Y  I  N  D  K  B
M  L  A  F  Z  S  L  C  E  N  H
D  A  N  A  G  R  O  C  J  I  V
```

The modern incarnation of a classic design, the Incom **T-70 X-wing** fighter is the signature combat craft of the Resistance forces in their fight against the First Order.

MISSING PIECE

Find the square that completes the picture.

A

B

C

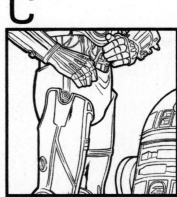

SECRET CODE

Using the secret code decipher the message.

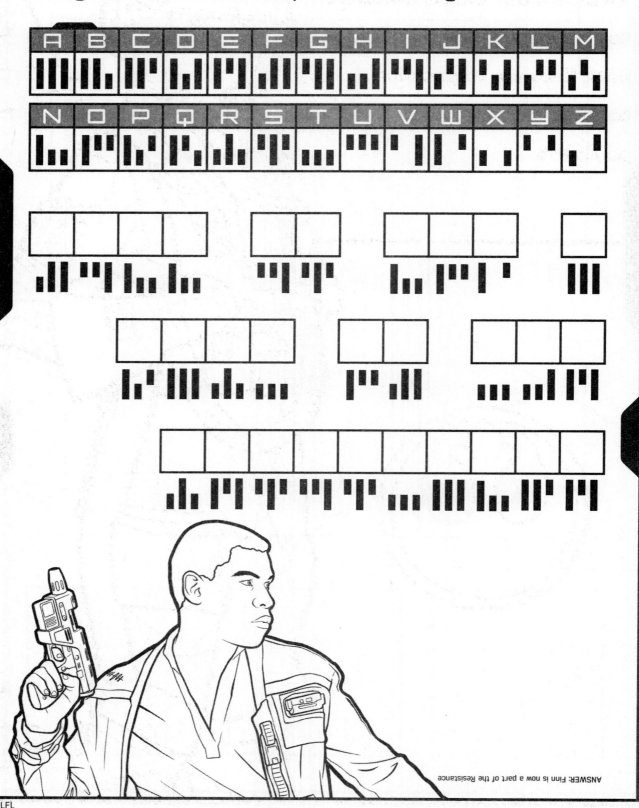

© LFL

A skilled A-wing interceptor pilot flying for the Resistance, **TALLIE** must escort bombers to keep enemy ships off them until they are in position to drop their explosive payloads.

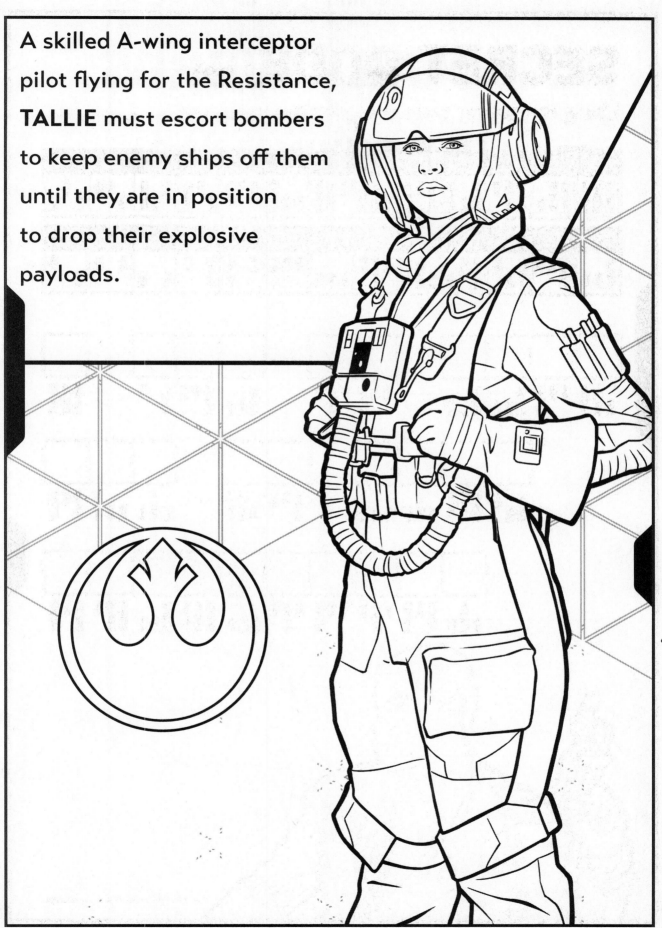

HOW MANY WORDS

See how many words you can make from the letters in:

LUKE SKYWALKER

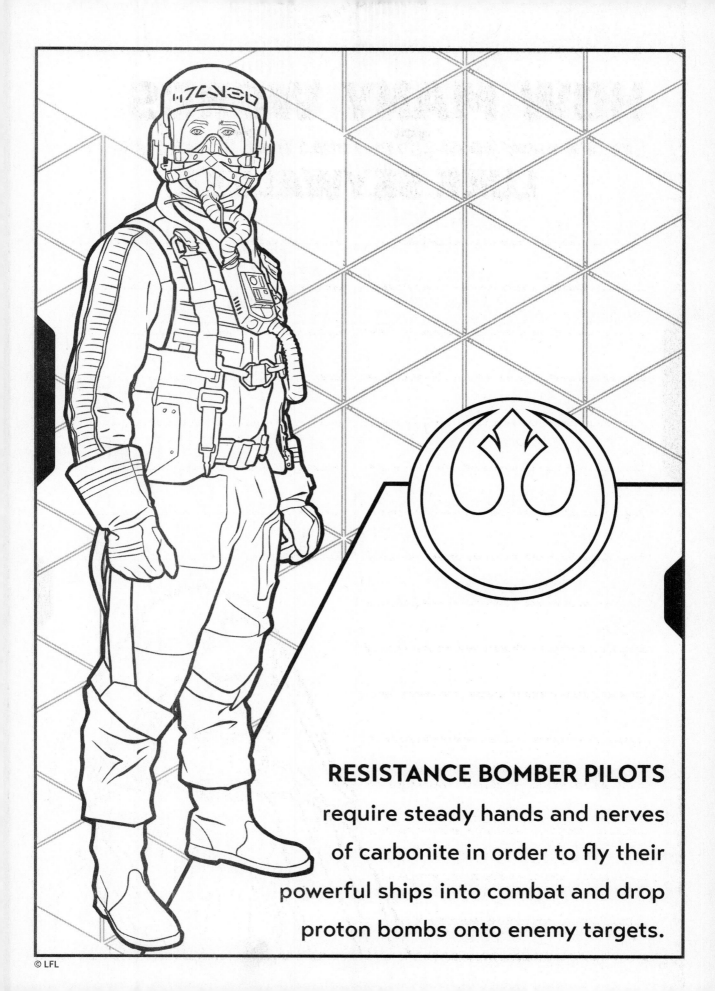

RESISTANCE BOMBER PILOTS
require steady hands and nerves
of carbonite in order to fly their
powerful ships into combat and drop
proton bombs onto enemy targets.

© LFL

WORD SEARCH

Find the words listed in the puzzle below.

LIGHTSABRE	JEDI
KNIGHT	FORCE
GENERAL	ADMIRAL
ORGANA	ACKBAR

```
Z  M  U  X  W  Z  E  R  K  T  Z
A  F  Z  R  K  N  R  A  D  P  R
S  O  L  A  K  B  D  C  Z  A
J  R  A  E  I  R  A  M  J  S  B
L  C  R  W  G  I  S  I  V  Y  K
R  E  E  I  H  T  T  R  F  E  C
T  V  N  J  T  F  H  A  N  O  A
G  P  E  W  H  U  G  L  I  H  A
M  K  G  J  E  Y  I  N  D  K  B
M  L  A  F  Z  S  L  C  E  N  H
D  A  N  A  G  R  O  C  J  I  V
```

DESIGN PAGE

Design your own Resistance soldier.

SECTOR GRID

Use the grid to help you draw the picture.

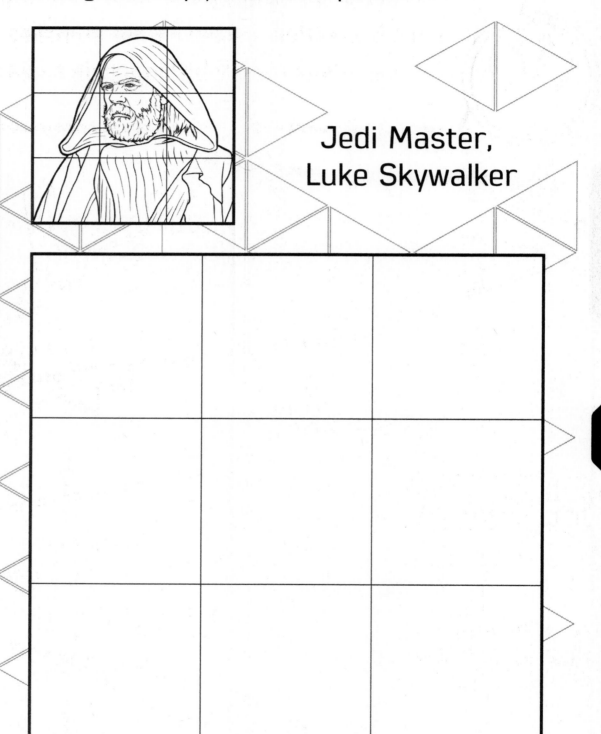

Jedi Master,
Luke Skywalker

A reliable starfighter model used by the
Resistance and dating back to the struggle
between Empire and Rebellion, the **A-wing** is
a nimble, wedge-shaped fighter propelled to
incredible speeds by large twin engines.

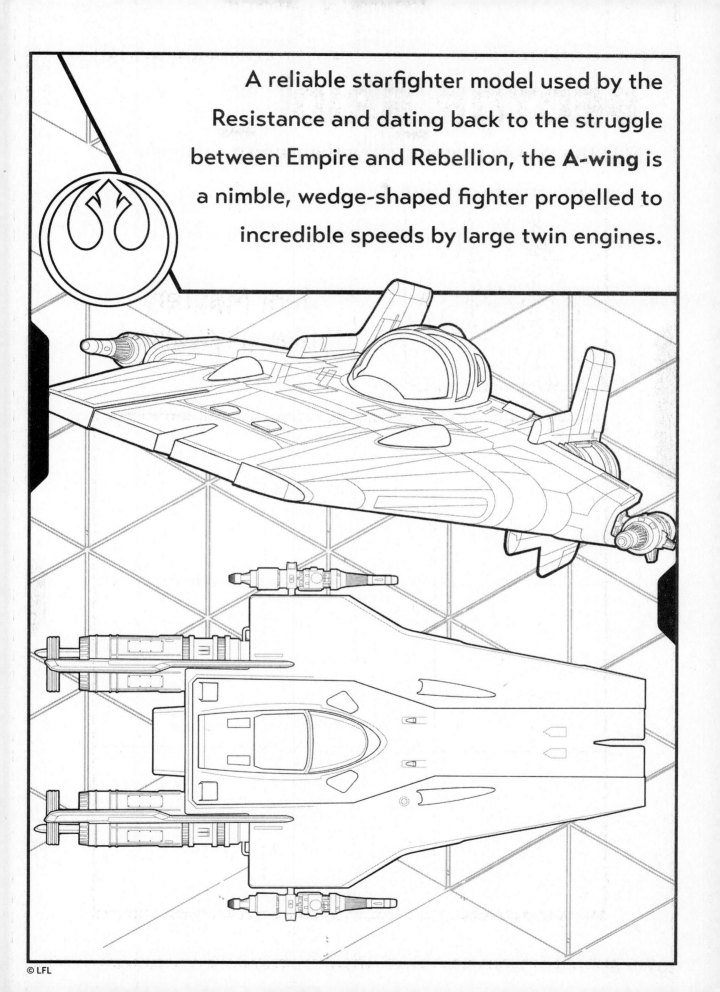

IMPOSTER

Find the X-wing that is different, that is the imposter.

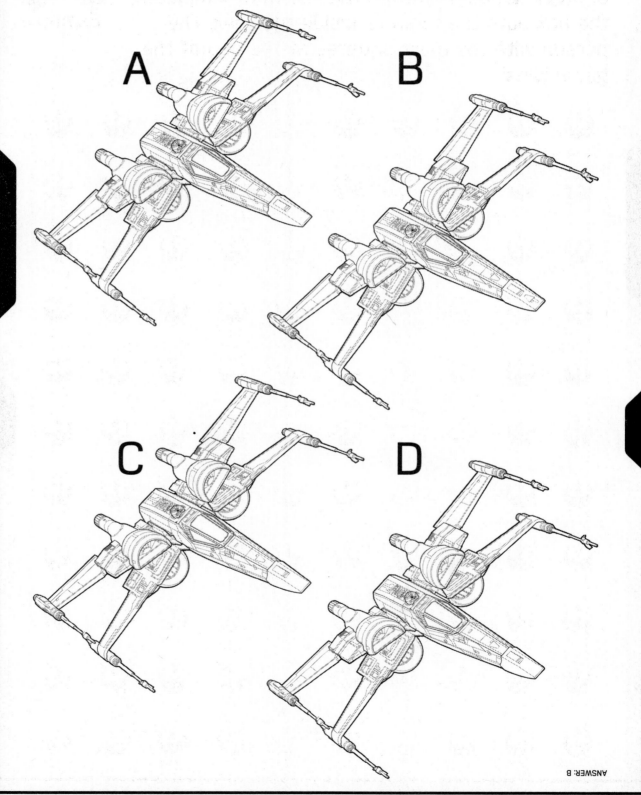

A

B

C

D

SQUARES

Taking turns, connect a line from one symbol to another. Whoever makes the line that completes the box puts their initials inside that box. The person with the most squares at the end of the game wins!

Example

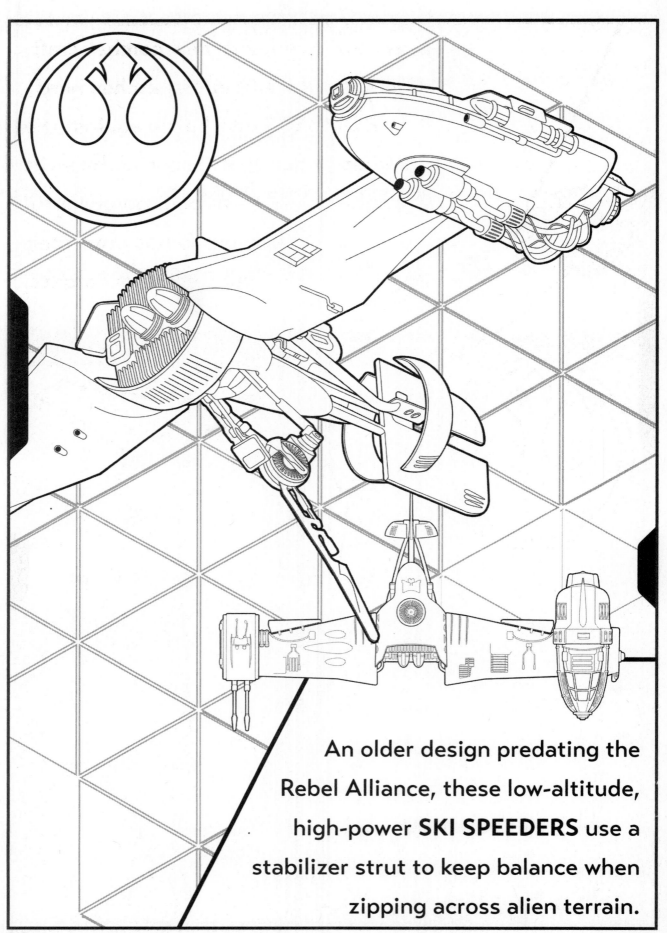

An older design predating the
Rebel Alliance, these low-altitude,
high-power **SKI SPEEDERS** use a
stabilizer strut to keep balance when
zipping across alien terrain.

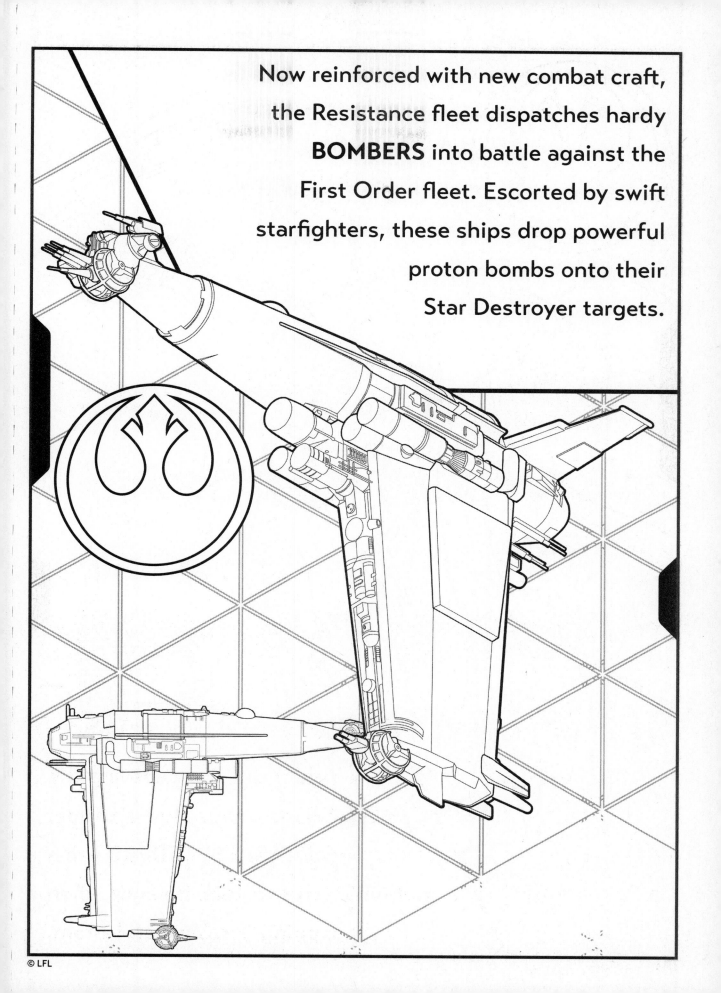

Now reinforced with new combat craft, the Resistance fleet dispatches hardy **BOMBERS** into battle against the First Order fleet. Escorted by swift starfighters, these ships drop powerful proton bombs onto their Star Destroyer targets.

MISSING PIECE

Find the square that completes the picture.

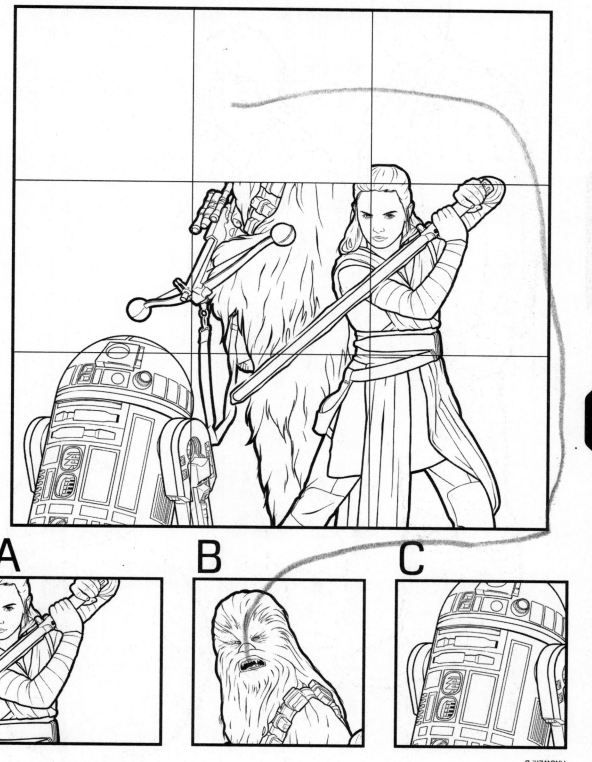

A

B

C

ANSWER: B

SECRET CODE

Using the secret code decipher the message.

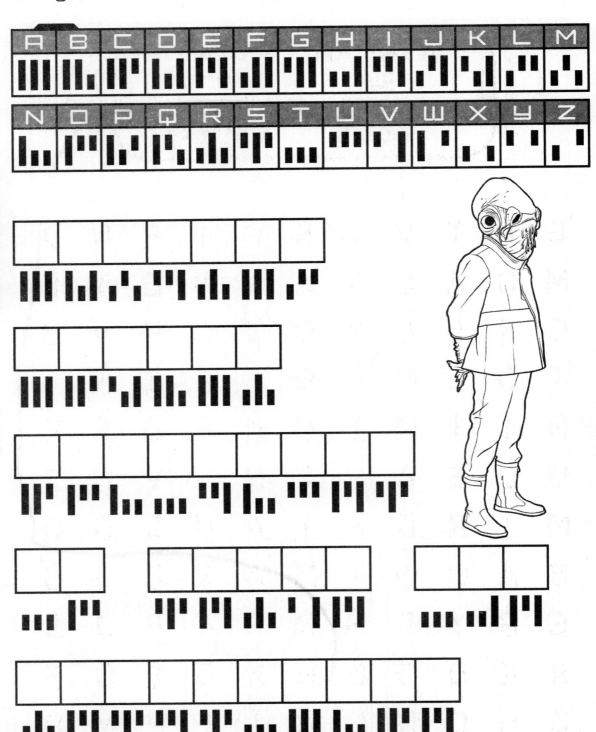

WORD SEARCH

Find the words listed in the puzzle below.

SKYWALKER
REY
DROID
TALLIE

JEDI
FALCON
COMMAND
BOMBERS

```
E  F  T  V  Z  K  C  I  P  N  J
M  D  A  C  K  A  X  N  O  T  E
Q  R  L  L  Y  Q  Y  C  R  V  D
T  O  L  M  C  Q  L  E  Z  K  I
B  I  I  M  T  O  K  E  D  F  K
O  D  E  A  F  L  N  N  V  H  J
M  T  R  D  A  Y  A  U  G  D  Q
B  A  Q  W  I  M  A  P  B  J  S
E  G  Y  F  M  N  P  R  F  J  S
R  K  D  O  B  H  X  D  E  C  F
S  H  C  D  C  C  I  E  H  Y  D
```

TIC-TAC-TOE

Challenge a friend to a game of tic-tac-toe.

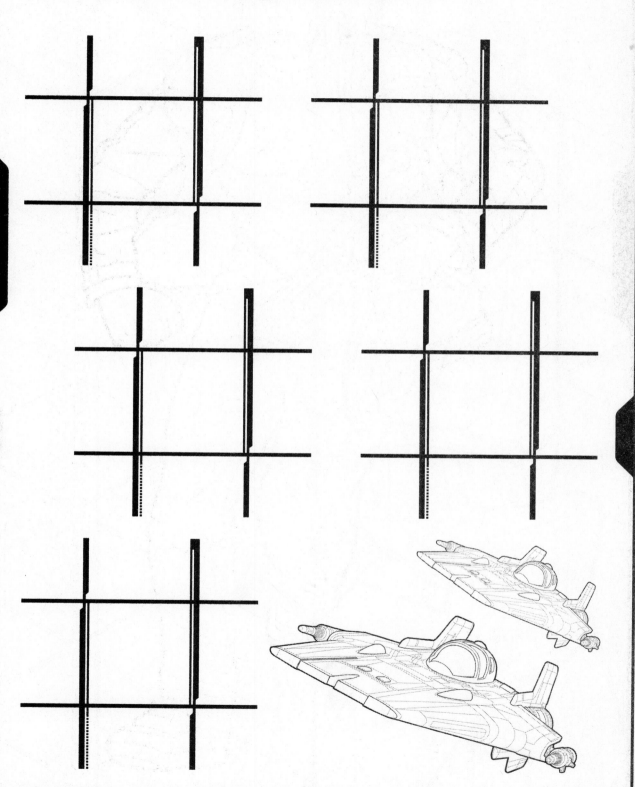

DESIGN PAGE

Draw a Wookiee.

TRACER

Use the lines to help you draw Admiral Ackbar.

HOW MANY WORDS

See how many words you can make from the letters in:

ADMIRAL ACKBAR

DRANET

SECTOR GRID

Use the grid to help you draw the picture.

Finn

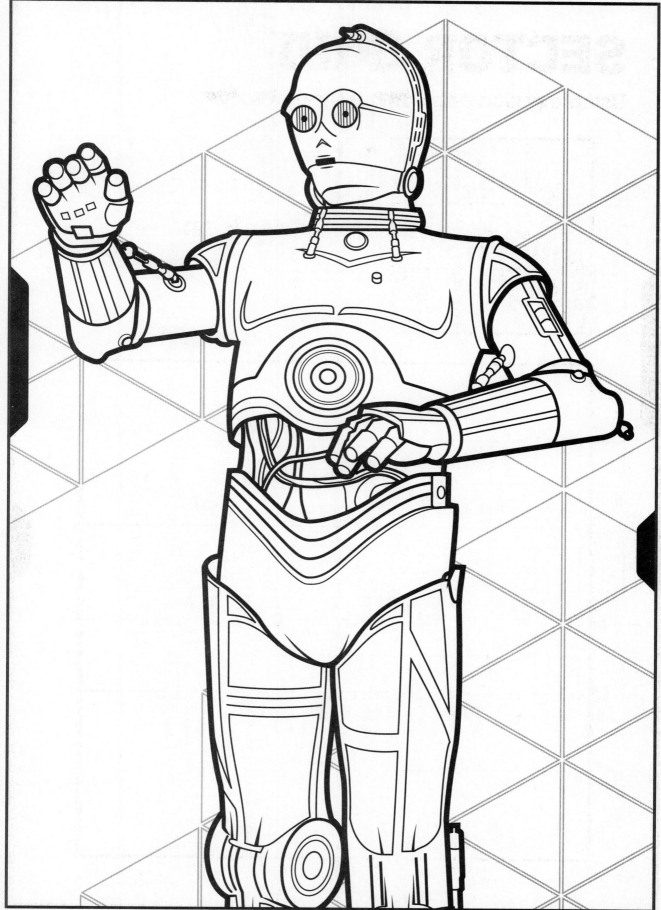

SECRET CODE

Using the secret code decipher the message.

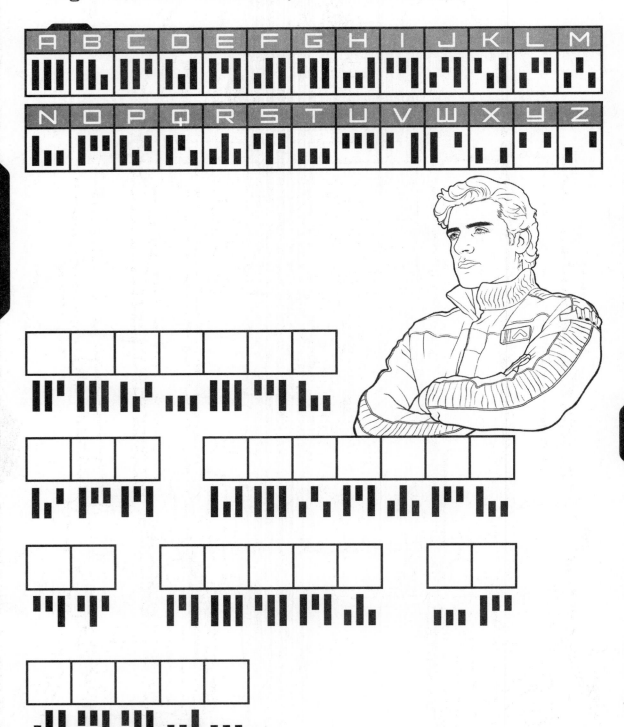

IMPOSTER

Find the real Finn that is different, the others are imposters.

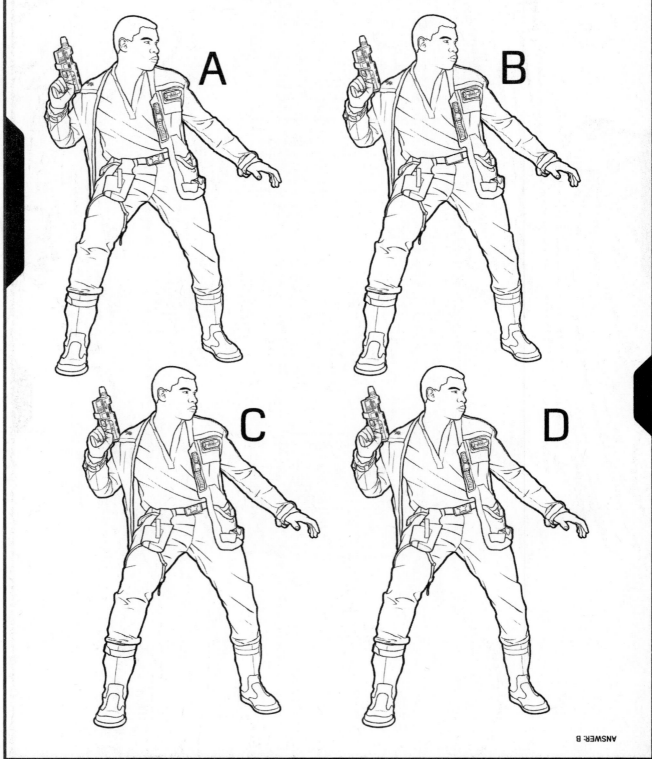

A

B

C

D

WORD SEARCH

Find the words listed in the puzzle below.

WOOKIEE
CORELLIAN
HYPERSPACE
JEDI

COPILOT
FALCON
MASTER
FORCE

```
Q N R F C X W B C Q H
E O E S L F E L I Y O
E C T E U D R Q P U E
I L S I F R D E Y L B
K A A X D F R H Y W J
O F M Y Y S K U O N E
O F S Q P C G N B Q D
W E R A Q V W G X Y I
B P C O P F O R C E S
U E C O R E L L I A N
C O P I L O T K G K P
```

TIC-TAC-TOE

Challenge a friend to a game of tic-tac-toe.

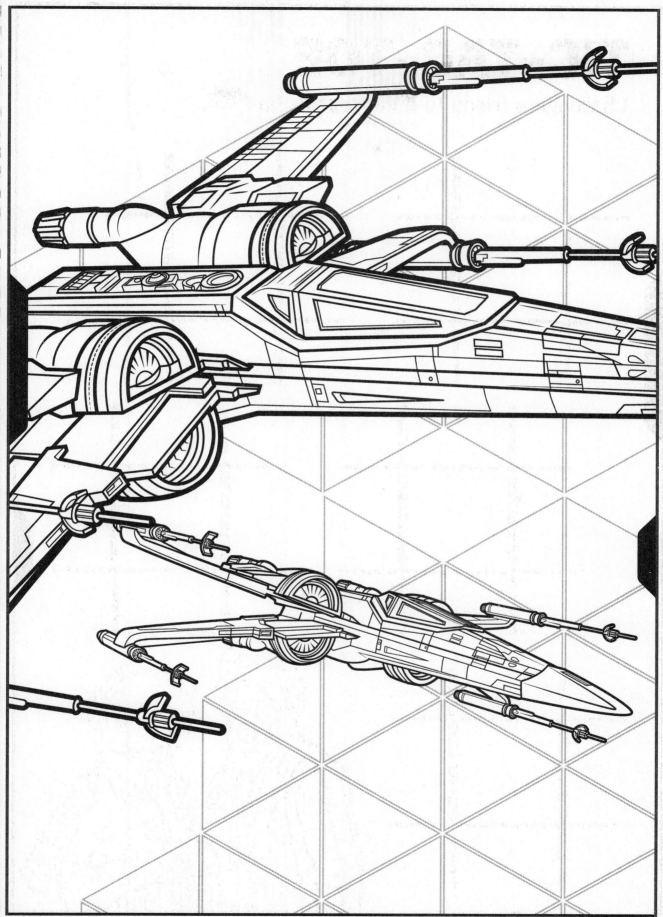

TRACER

Use the lines to help you draw R2-D2.

DESIGN PAGE

Draw an alien.

SQUARES

Taking turns, connect a line from one symbol to another. Whoever makes the line that completes the box puts their initials inside that box. The person with the most squares at the end of the game wins!

Example

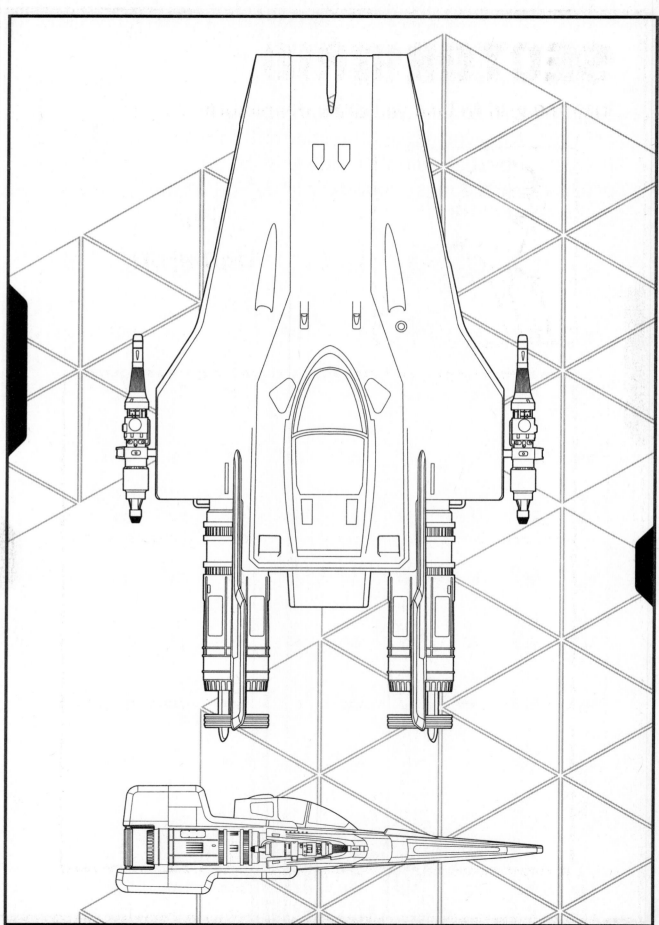

SECTOR GRID

Use the grid to help you draw the picture.

Poe
Dameron

MISSING PIECE

Find the square that completes the picture.

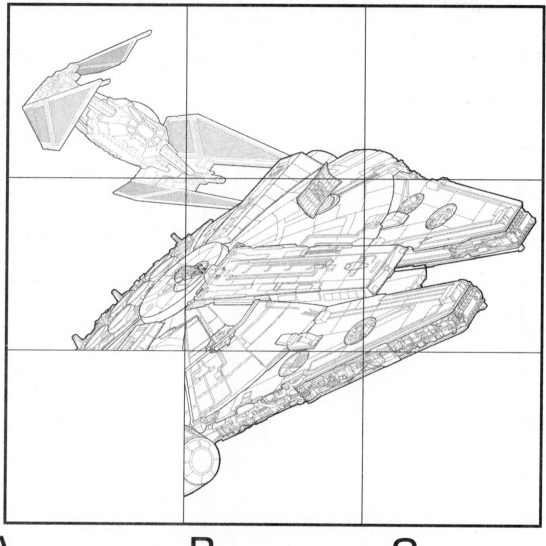

A

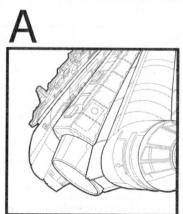

B

C

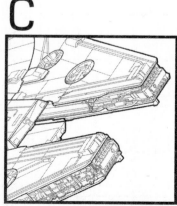

HOW MANY WORDS

See how many words you can make from the letters in:

CAPTAIN POE DAMERON

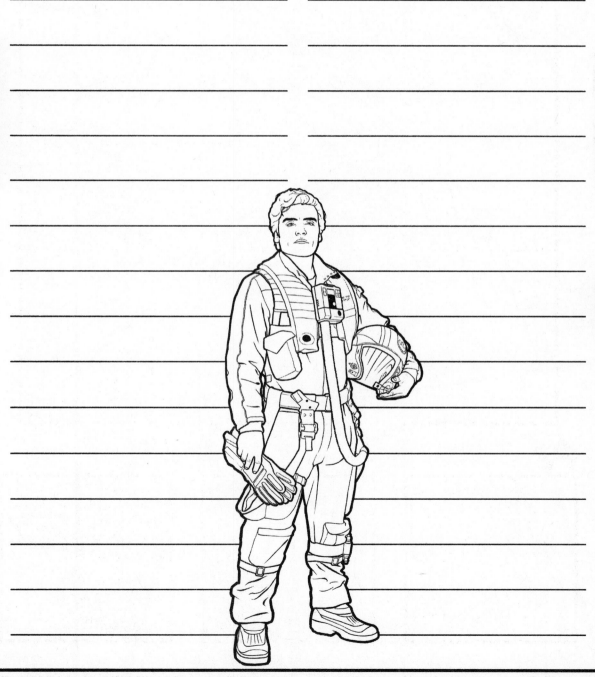

SECRET CODE

Using the secret code decipher the message.

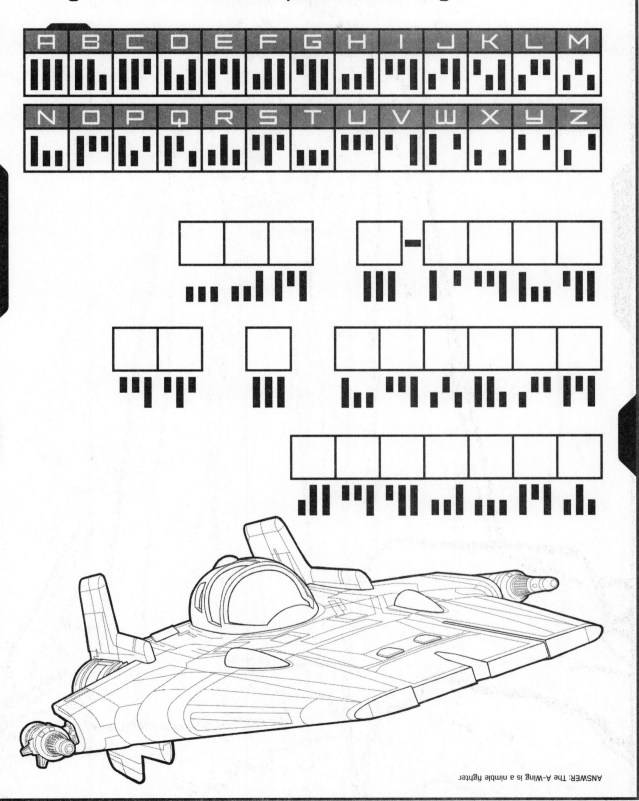

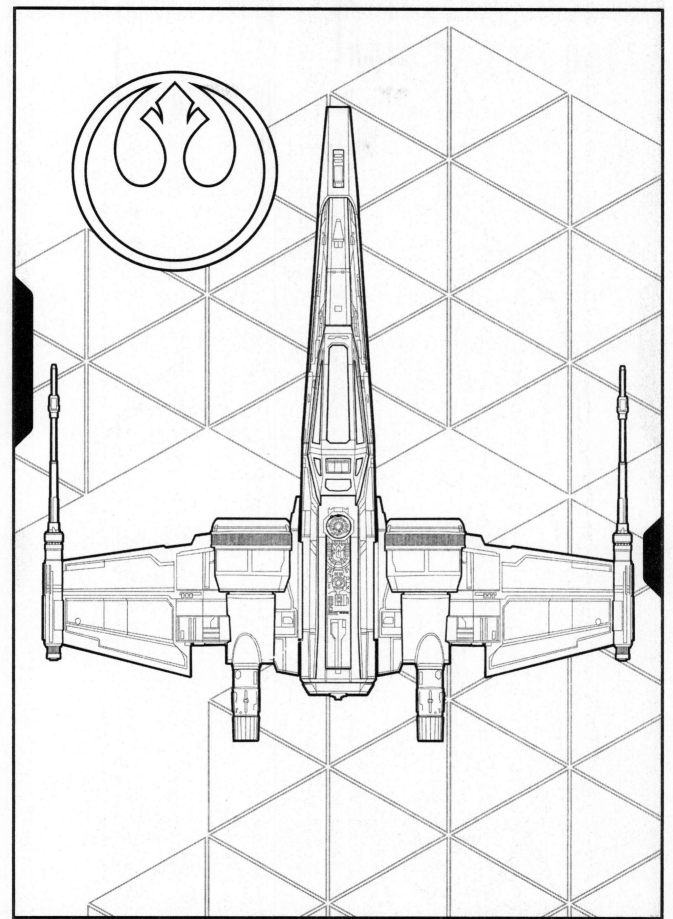

IMPOSTER

Find the Luke Skywalker that is different, that is the real Luke.

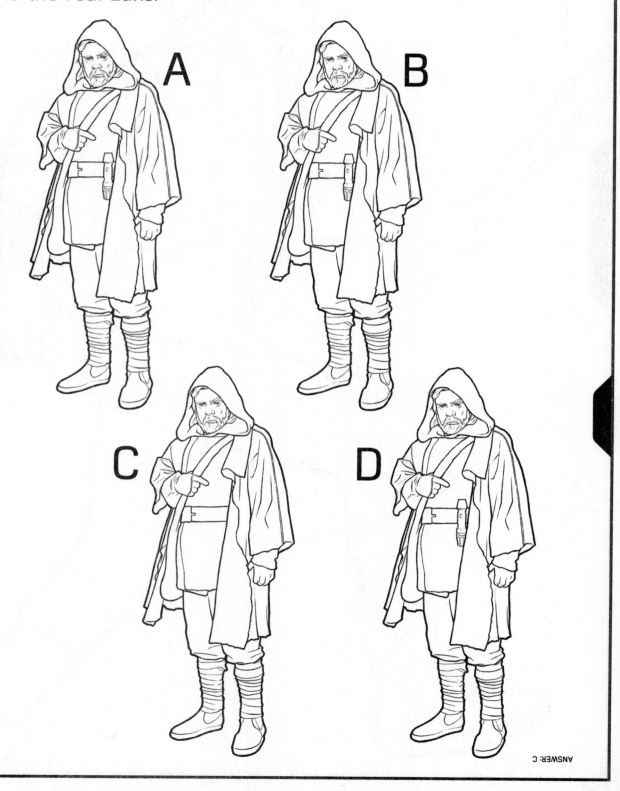

© LFL

TRACER

Use the lines to help you draw Chewbacca.

HOW MANY WORDS

See how many words you can make from the letters in:

RESISTANCE PILOT

_____   _____

_____   _____

_____   _____

_____   _____

_____   _____

_____   _____

_____   _____

_____

_____

_____

_____

_____

_____

_____

SECRET CODE

Using the secret code decipher the message.

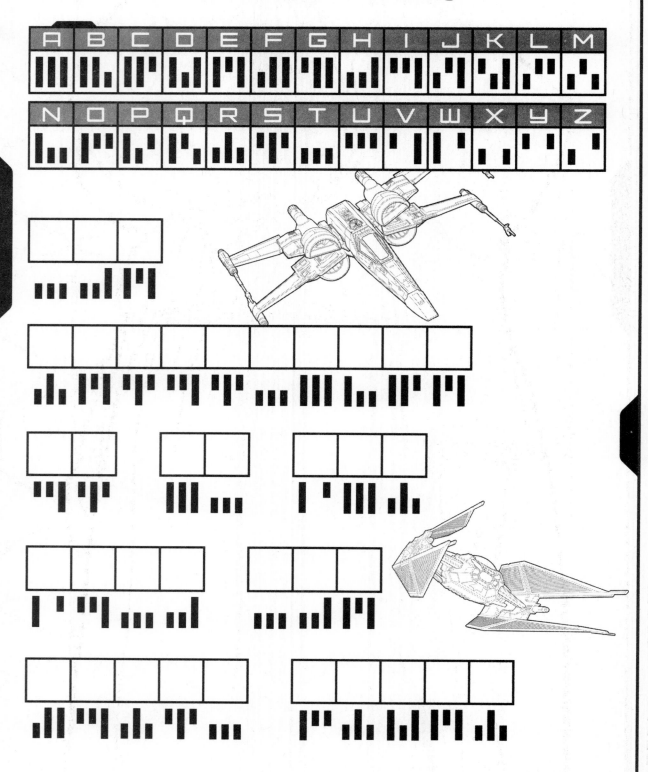

MISSING PIECE

Find the square that completes the picture.

A

B

C

SQUARES

Taking turns, connect a line from one symbol to another. Whoever makes the line that completes the box puts their initials inside that box. The person with the most squares at the end of the game wins!

Example

DESIGN PAGE

Design your own speeder bike.

SECTOR GRID

Use the grid to help you draw the picture.

Leia
Organa

TIC-TAC-TOE

Challenge a friend to a game of tic-tac-toe.

WORD SEARCH

Find the words listed in the puzzle below.

CAPTAIN	PILOT
GENERAL	SOLDIER
FIGHTER	BLASTER
PLANET	GALAXY

M F G L F I G H T E R
S N R A L Q T R T B M
F I Y B L F J E Z H G
Y A W F P A O H U A E
U T O S P U X D D R N
Q P L K L Q Y Y P J E
R A B L A S T E R T R
R C M N N A R Q O O A
W I K R E K I S J L L
F R P D T J R S A I A
S O L D I E R C D P C

MISSING PIECE

Find the square that completes the picture.

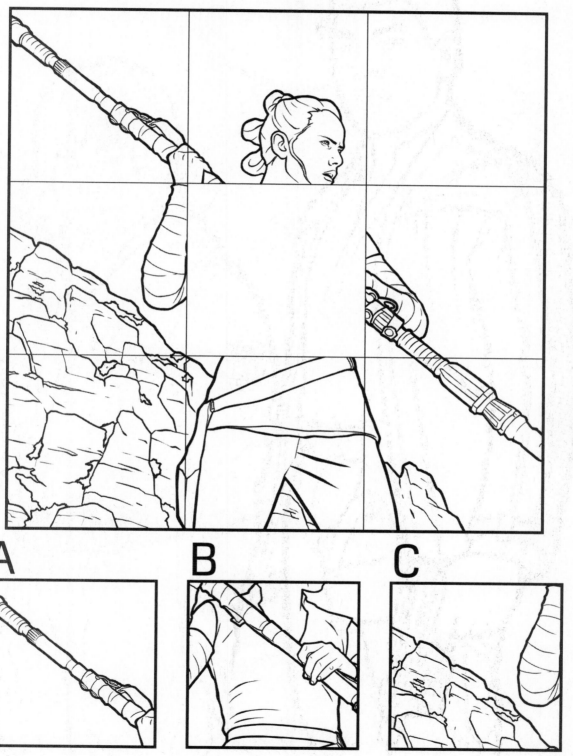

A

B

C

IMPOSTER

Find the R2-D2 that is different, that is the real R2-D2.

A

B

C

D

HOW MANY WORDS

See how many words you can make from the letters in:

REY, CHEWBACCA & R2-D2

DESIGN PAGE

Design your own lightsabre.

WORD SEARCH

Find the words listed in the puzzle below.

GENERAL HUX
TIE SILENCER
ASTROMECH
STARSHIP

JUSTICE
LEGIONS
WEAPON
FINALIZER

```
O  S  J  C  I  A  V  G  H  Z  N
R  E  Z  I  L  A  N  I  F  W  O
C  P  I  H  S  R  A  T  S  Y  P
S  T  B  E  C  I  T  S  U  J  A
A  S  T  R  O  M  E  C  H  N  E
J  D  O  V  Q  X  V  P  W  O  W
L  L  E  G  I  O  N  S  P  Z  Y
N  A  P  Z  T  G  B  C  N  Q  A
O  X  U  H  L  A  R  E  N  E  G
S  H  Y  K  S  Z  N  W  X  J  S
R  E  C  N  E  L  I  S  E  I  T
```

IMPOSTER

Find the Flame Trooper that is different,
that is the imposter.

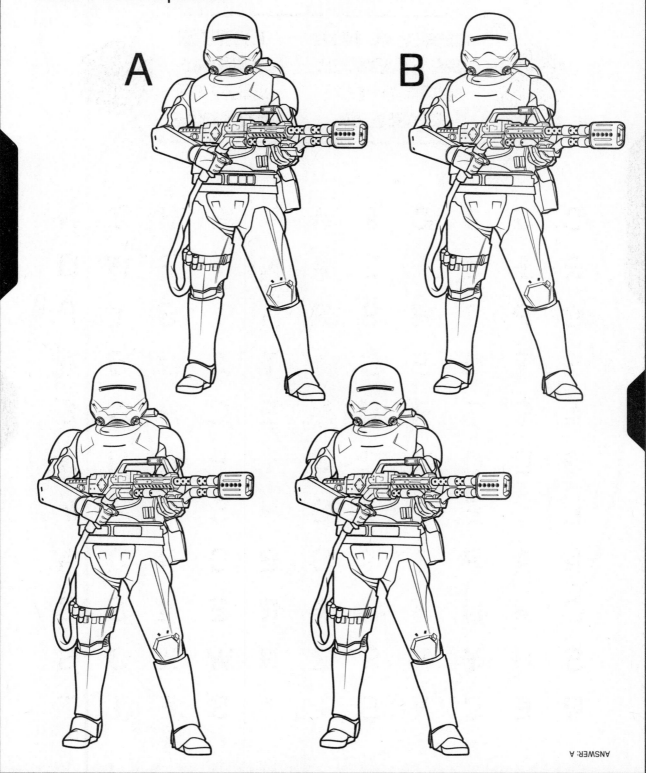

A

B

ANSWER: A

MAZE

Help the First Order TIE Fighters find the X-wing fighter.

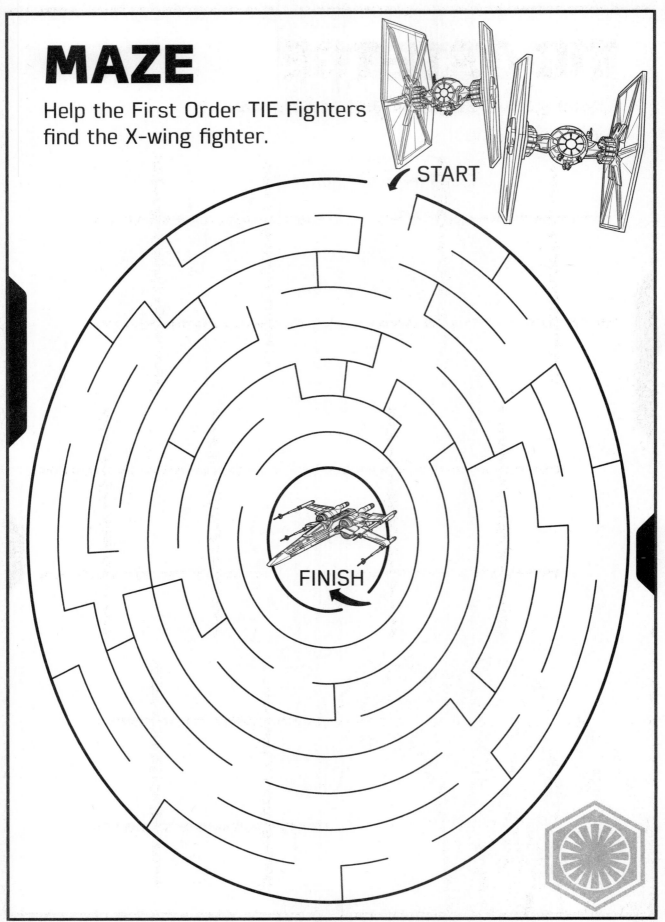

START

FINISH

TIC-TAC-TOE

Challenge a friend to a game of tic-tac-toe.

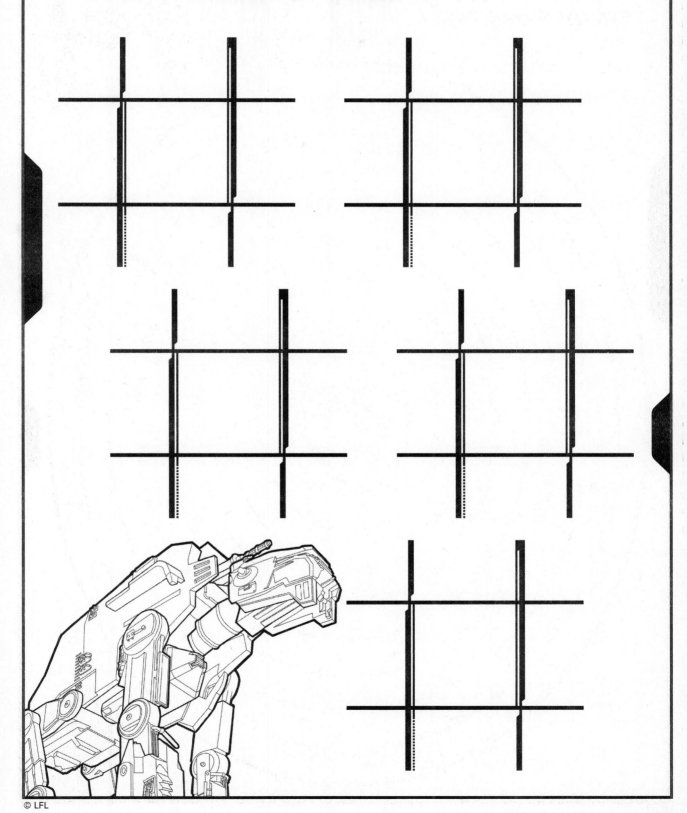

SQUARES

Taking turns, connect a line from one symbol to another. Whoever makes the line that completes the box puts their initials inside that box. The person with the most squares at the end of the game wins!

Example

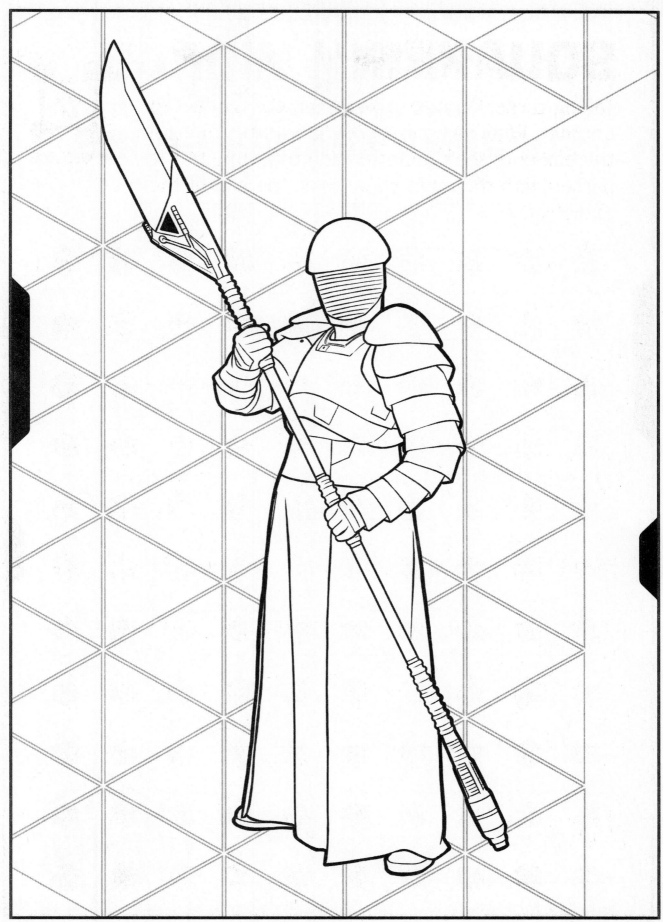

HOW MANY WORDS

See how many words you can make from the letters in:

SUPREME LEADER SNOKE

FOLLOW THE PATH

Using the letters, in order, from the word **GENERAL HUX**,
follow the correct path to find your way through the maze.

START

G	E	N	J	K	O	M	Z
O	S	E	R	A	L	H	S
R	C	E	F	C	B	U	X
M	A	E	H	E	G		
R	O	F	E	N	A		
C	P	L	R	B	N		
L	G	F	A	R	S		
R	C	Y	L	H	U		
R	I	E	J	E	X		

FINISH

© LFL

Lumbering armored beasts that are the latest generation in walkers, these **AT-M6 WALKERS** are enormous transports that help the First Order secure the worlds of its expanding territories.

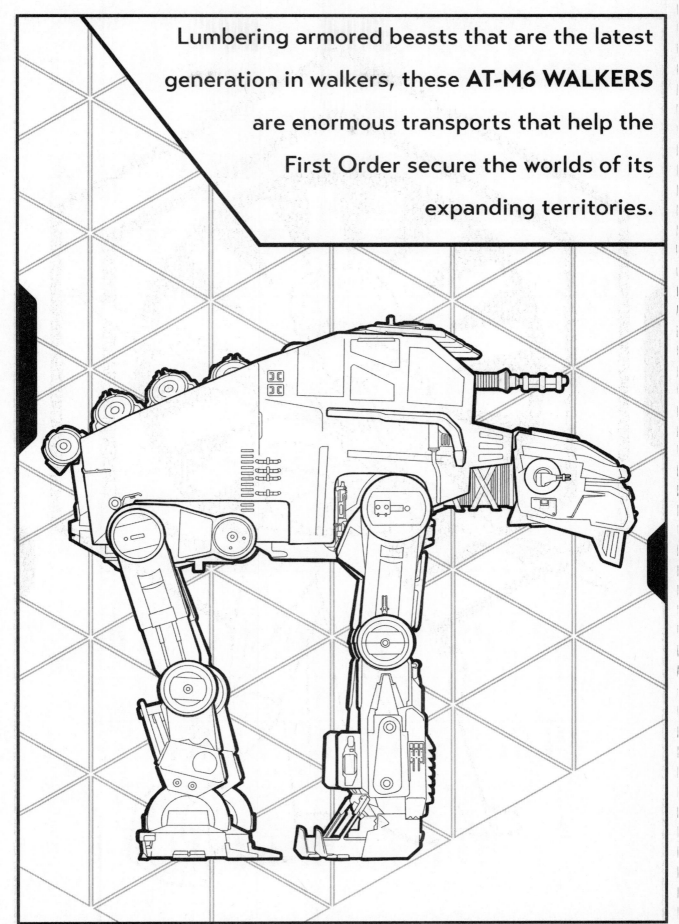

SECRET CODE

Using the secret code decipher the message.

© LFL

MISSING PIECE

Find the square that completes the picture.

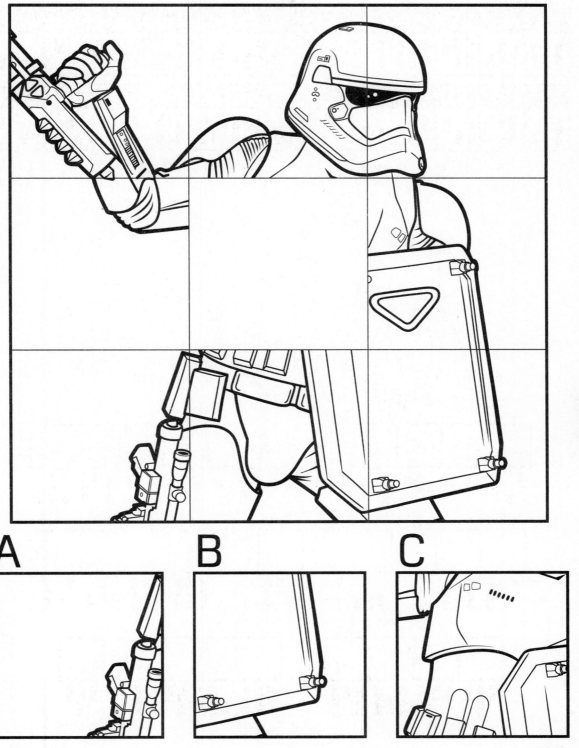

A

B

C

© LFL

DESIGN PAGE

Design an alien.

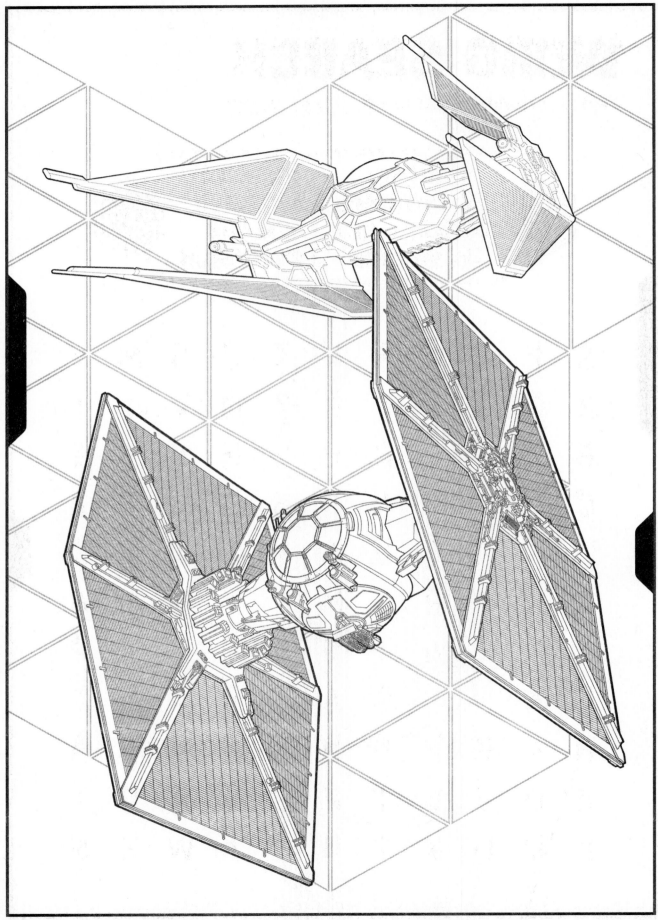

WORD SEARCH

Find the words listed in the puzzle below.

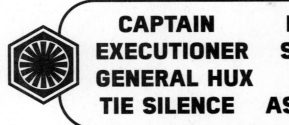

CAPTAIN   PHASMA
EXECUTIONER   STARSHIP
GENERAL HUX   KNIGHT
TIE SILENCE   ASTROMECH

```
E  F  P  P  R  V  T  J  S  M  Y
X  C  I  G  E  R  Z  Q  V  I  I
E  G  H  E  C  P  V  H  Y  T  S
C  L  S  N  N  F  X  C  V  T  Z
U  G  R  E  E  A  Y  E  K  H  C
T  D  A  R  L  M  R  M  V  G  A
I  N  T  A  I  S  V  O  H  I  P
O  X  S  L  S  A  E  R  A  N  T
N  K  K  H  E  H  E  T  P  K  A
E  O  V  U  I  P  O  S  R  D  I
R  U  U  X  T  D  K  A  W  X  N
```

SQUARES

Taking turns, connect a line from one symbol to another. Whoever makes the line that completes the box puts their initials inside that box. The person with the most squares at the end of the game wins!

Example

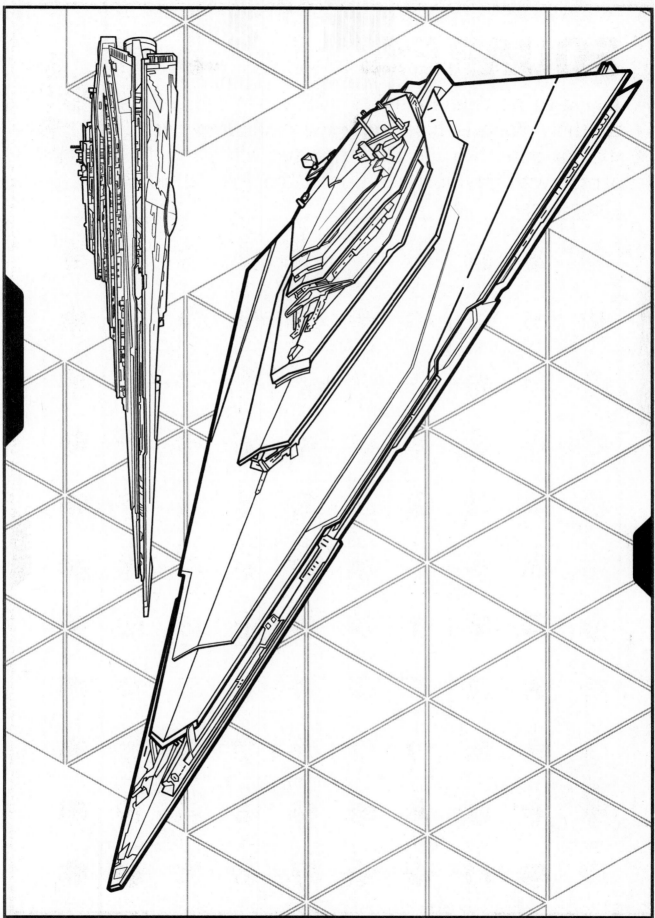

© LFL

MAZE

Find your way through the
maze to the First Order fleet.

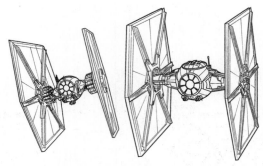

START

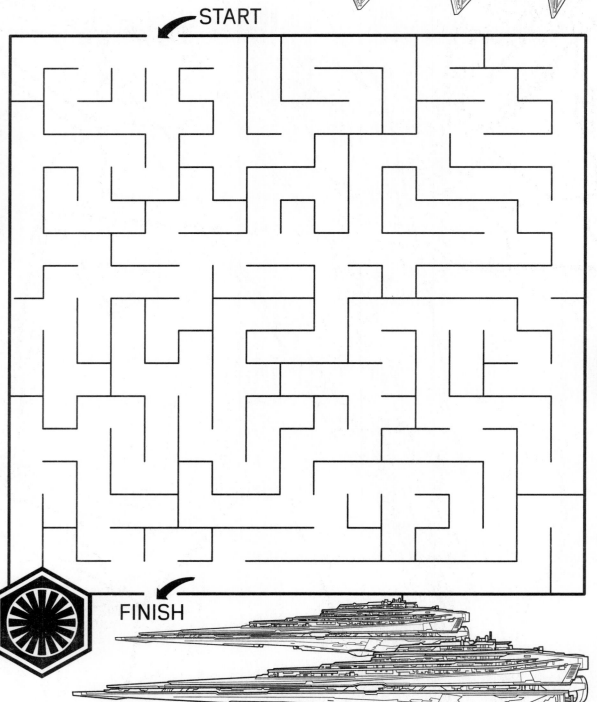

FINISH

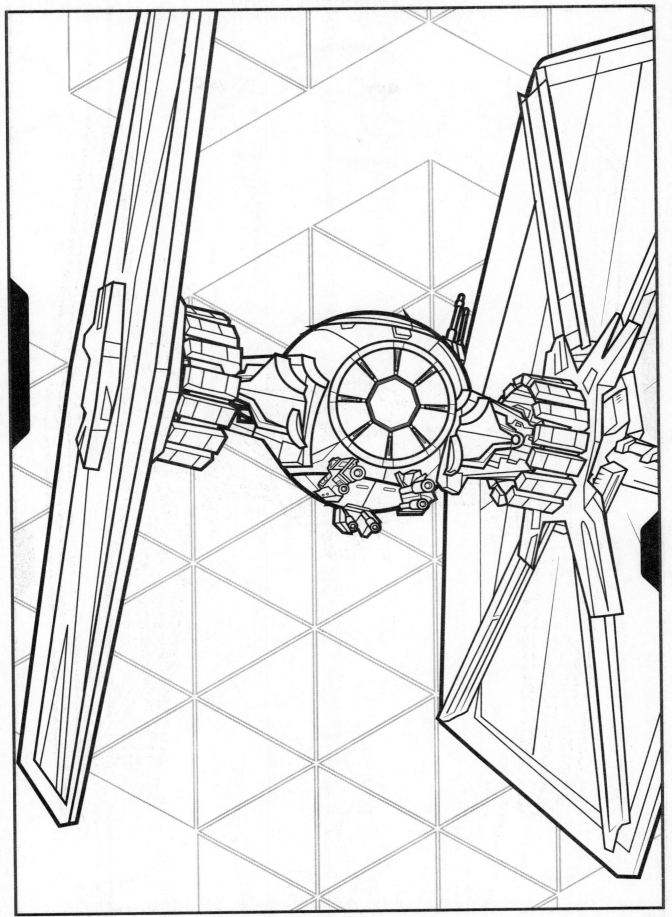

© LFL

FOLLOW THE PATH

Using the letters, in order, from the word **EXECUTIONER**, follow the correct path to find your way through the maze.

START

E	A	T	J
X	S	H	O

E	C	E	F	C	B

D	U	M	A	E	V	U	I

I	T	X	E	C	U	E	A

O	R	E	P	L	T	I	S

N	E	L	G	F	J	O	N

G	O	R	C	E	L	C	E

M	O	R	C	E	L	M	R

FINISH

© LFL

DESIGN PAGE

Design your own armored Walker.

MISSING PIECE

Find the square that completes the picture.

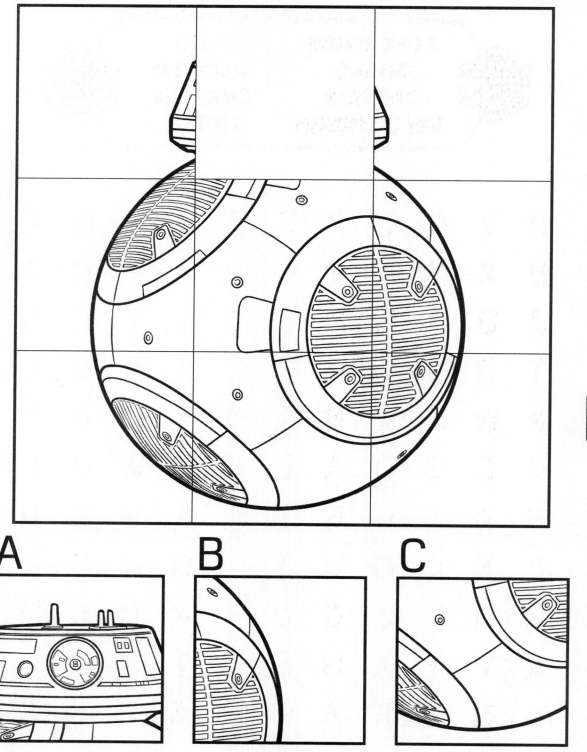

A

B

C

WORD SEARCH

Find the words listed in the puzzle below.

STAR WARS
GUARD
CAPTAIN
EXECUTIONER

ELITE
BLASTER
PHASMA
KNIGHT

```
D V G L P C F Z S G F
B X M A Z H D Y T C J
Z O G B M E L I T E S
T O B L A S T E R L L
X W N X N I A T P A C
Q C G Q A E U H W O L
B Z T H G I N K P C H
E X E C U T I O N E R
H Q Y G G U A R D L M
X V Y A H E T T Y C L
A B S R A W R A T S Q
```

HOW MANY WORDS

See how many words you can make from the letters in:
TIE FIGHTER

_____   _____

_____   _____

_____   _____

_____   _____

_____   _____

_____   _____

_____   _____

_____   _____

_____   _____

_____   _____

_____   _____

_____   _____

© LFL

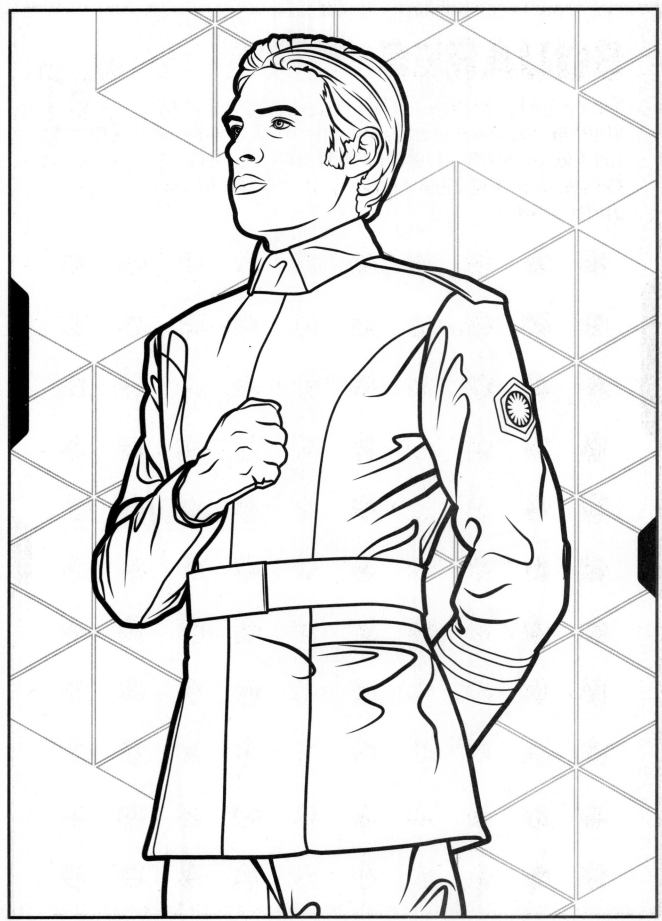

SQUARES

Taking turns, connect a line from one symbol to another. Whoever makes the line that completes the box puts their initials inside that box. The person with the most squares at the end of the game wins!

Example

TIC-TAC-TOE

Challenge a friend to a game of tic-tac-toe.

SECTOR GRID

Use the grid to help you draw the picture.

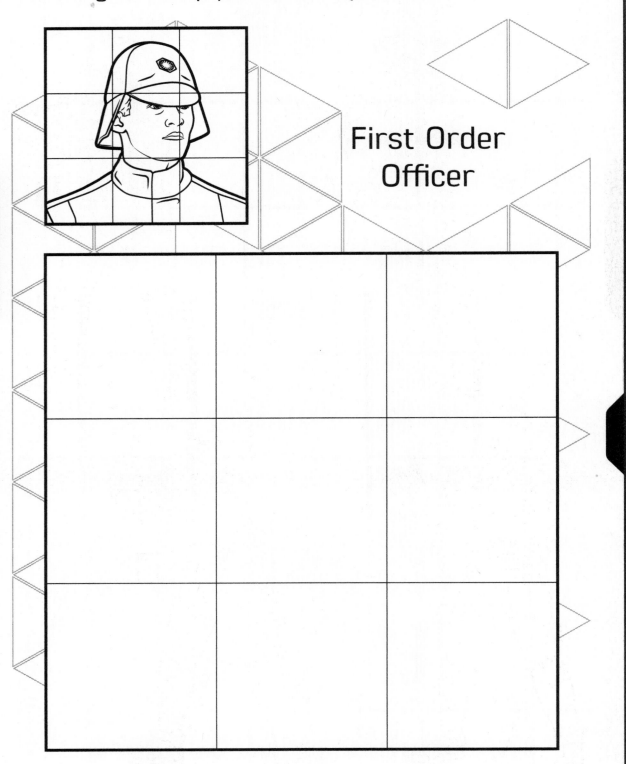

First Order
Officer

IMPOSTER

Find the Stormtrooper that is different, that is the imposter.

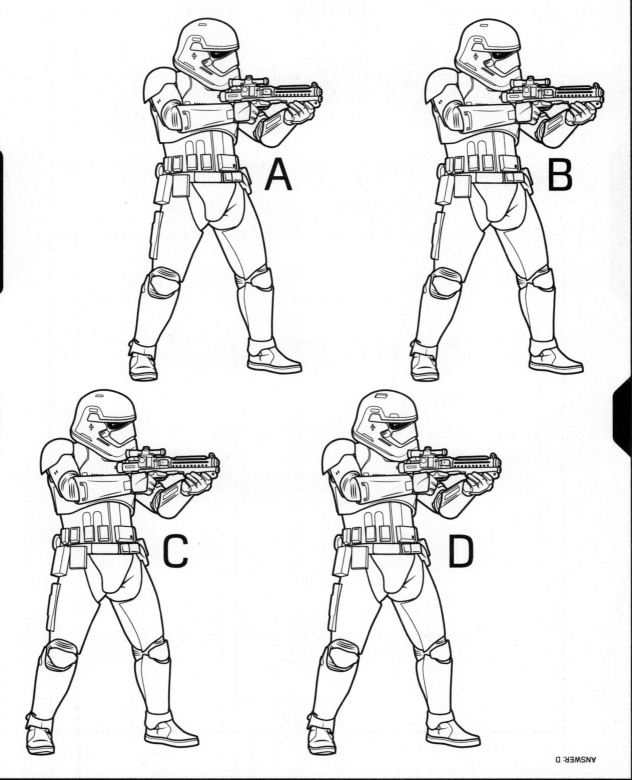

A

B

C

D

UNSCRAMBLE

Unscramble the letters listed to fit the spaces below.

XUENEGRAHL

_ _ _ _ _   _ _ _   _ _ _

STICENREILE

_ _ _   _ _ _ _ _ _ _ _

TRUCSTIDEON

_ _ _ _ _ _ _ _ _ _ _

THARSSIPS

_ _ _ _ _ _ _ _ _

SLATRILKER

_ _ _ _ _ _ _ _ _ _

© LFL

MAZE

Help the First Order catch the *Millennium Falcon*.

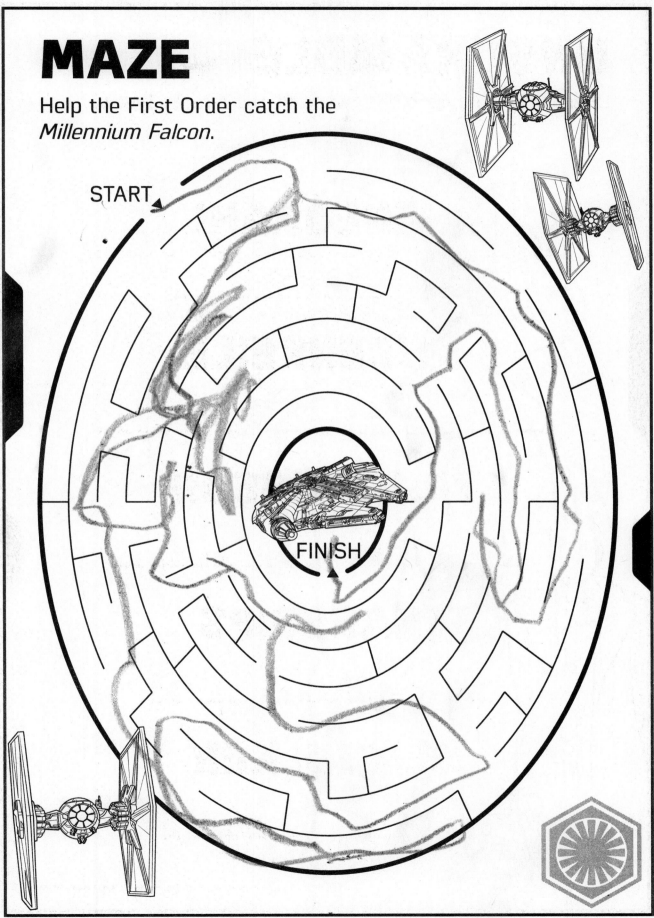

START

FINISH

FOLLOW THE PATH

Using the letters, in order, from the word **ASTROMECH**, follow the correct path to find your way through the maze.

START

A	S	T	R	K	O	M	Z
O	S	H	O	M	E	C	S
R	C	E	F	C	A	H	C
O	F	B	R	T	S	U	I
C	E	M	O	F	G	E	A
H	A	C	P	L	D	B	N
P	S	L	G	F	O	R	S
N	T	R	O	M	E	C	B
M	O	R	C	E	L	H	W

FINISH

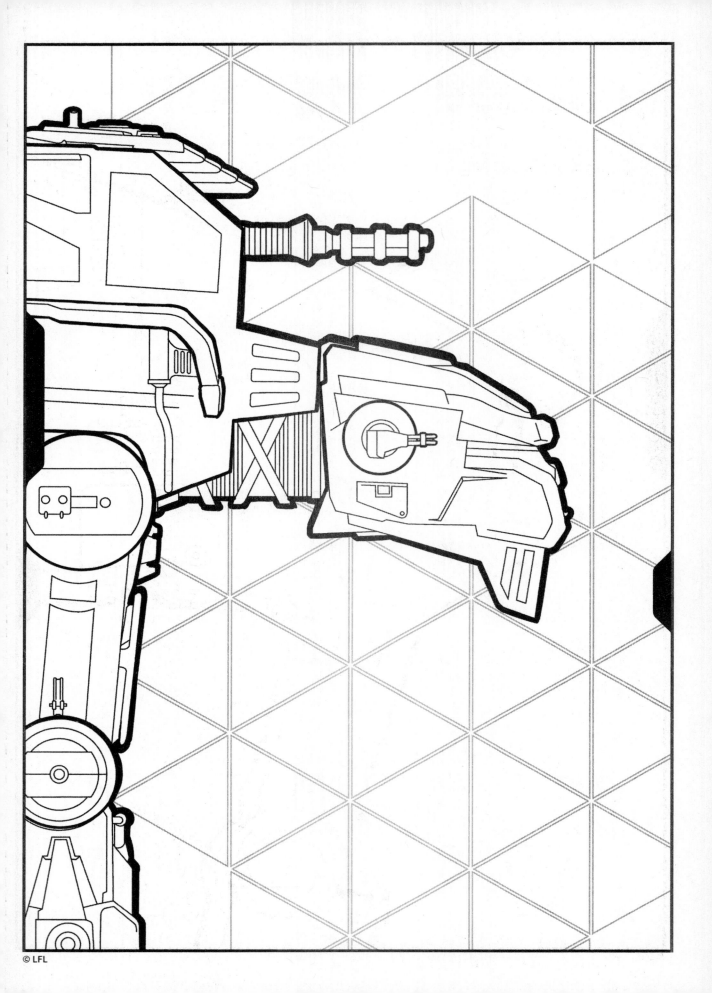

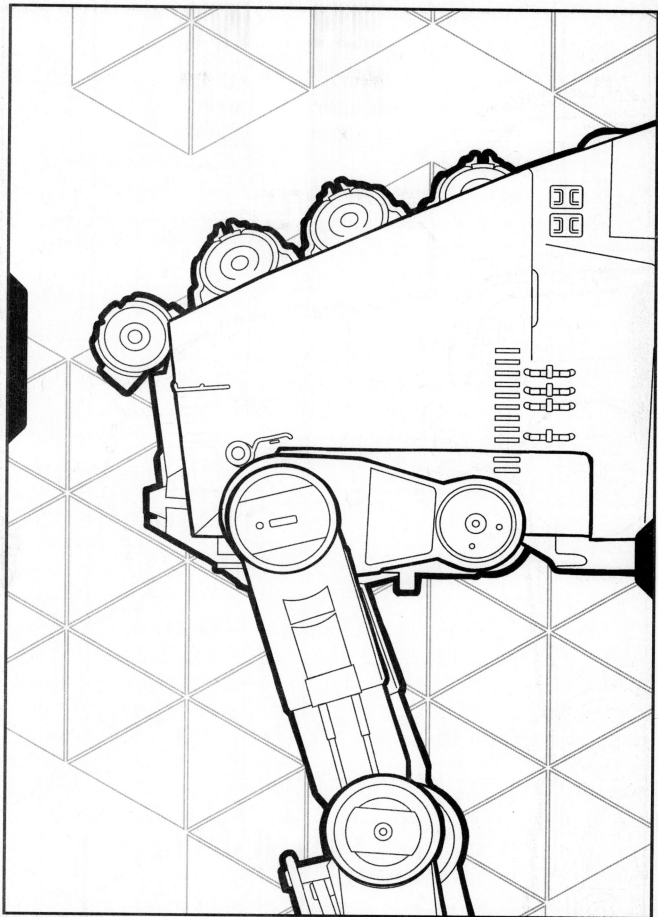

SECRET CODE

Using the secret code decipher the message.

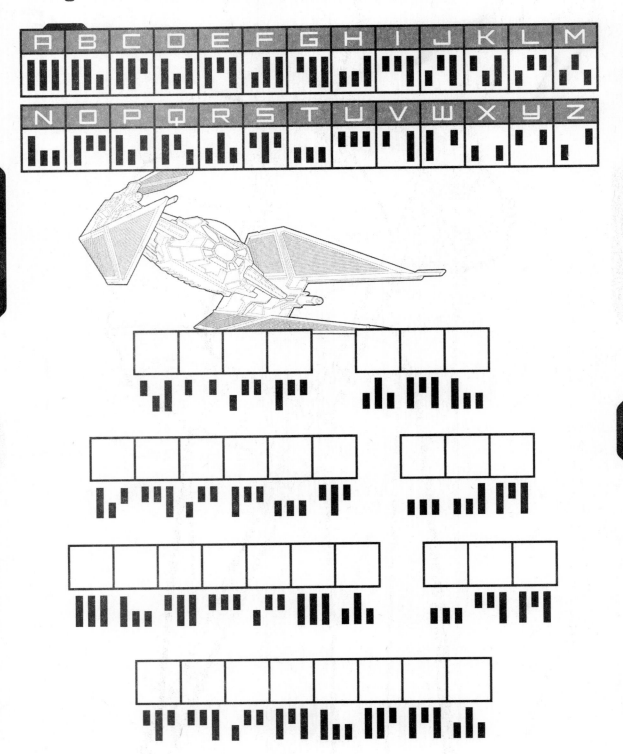

© LFL

© LFL

HOW MANY WORDS

See how many words you can make from the letters in:

STAR DESTROYER

SQUARES

Taking turns, connect a line from one symbol to another. Whoever makes the line that completes the box puts their initials inside that box. The person with the most squares at the end of the game wins!

Example

IMPOSTER

Find the General Amatige Hux that is different, he is the imposter.

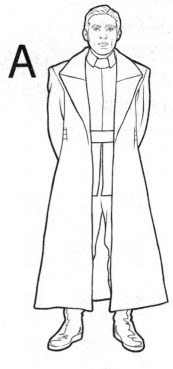

A

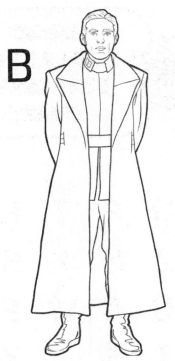

B

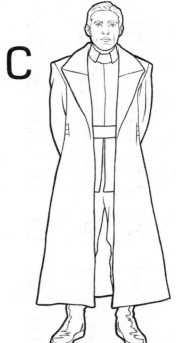

C

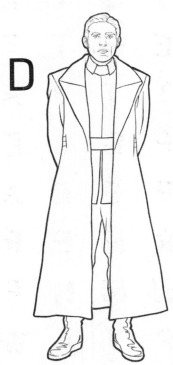

D

WORD SEARCH

Find the words listed in the puzzle below.

DROID
GALACTIC
STAR WARS
GUARD

TROOPER
EMPIRE
ELITE
BLASTER

```
T U P T K E M P I R E
I Z M X R L Z G W Q K
Q U C W F O I N X G X
R T S I X G O F T T N
H E W T T D W P K J J
E T T V A C R T E M Q
S P Q S E R A O Y R D
X P E R A L W L I I R
E R H E R L I A A D A
Z W M N F R B T R G U
X P Y A W H Q J E S G
```

TIC-TAC-TOE

Challenge a friend to a game of tic-tac-toe.

© LFL

MISSING PIECE

Find the square that completes the picture.

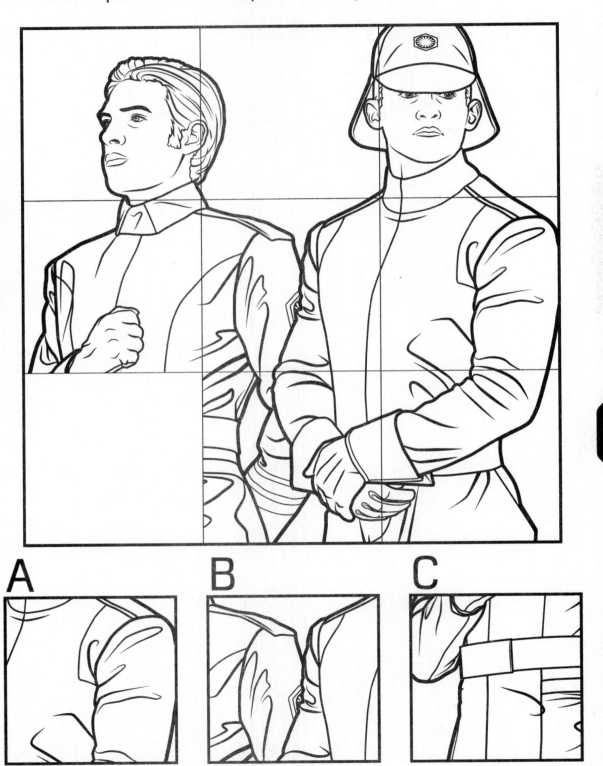

A

B

C

DESIGN PAGE

Design your own Praetorian Guard armor.

The First Order can operate effectively only with the absolute loyalty of its followers. Should any soldier be found guilty of treason, it is up to the **EXECUTIONERS** to dispense final justice.

MAZE

Help Kylo Ren find Rey.

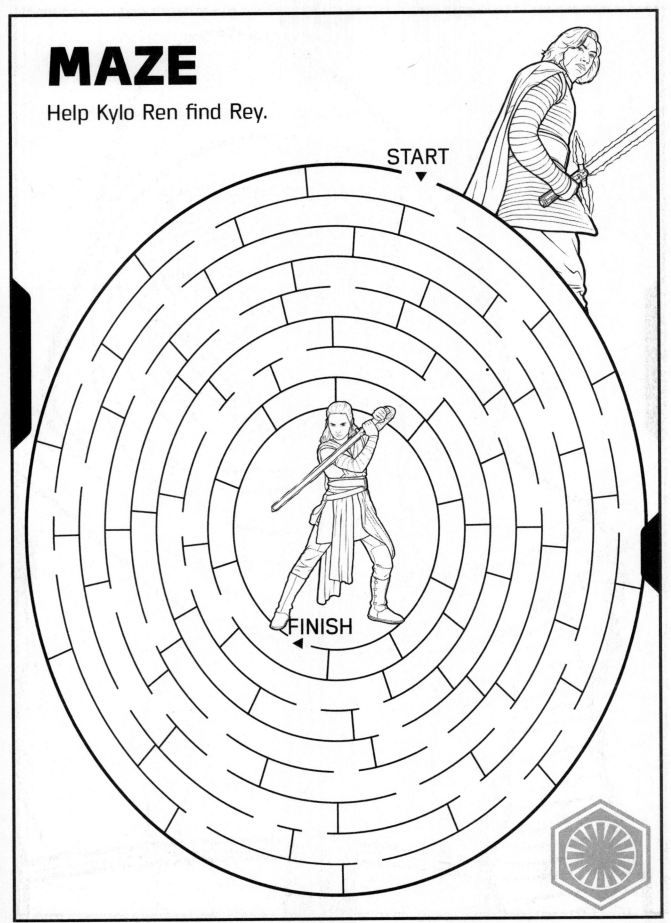

START

FINISH

SECTOR GRID

Use the grid to help you draw the picture.

First Order
Flame Trooper

SECRET CODE

Using the secret code decipher the message.

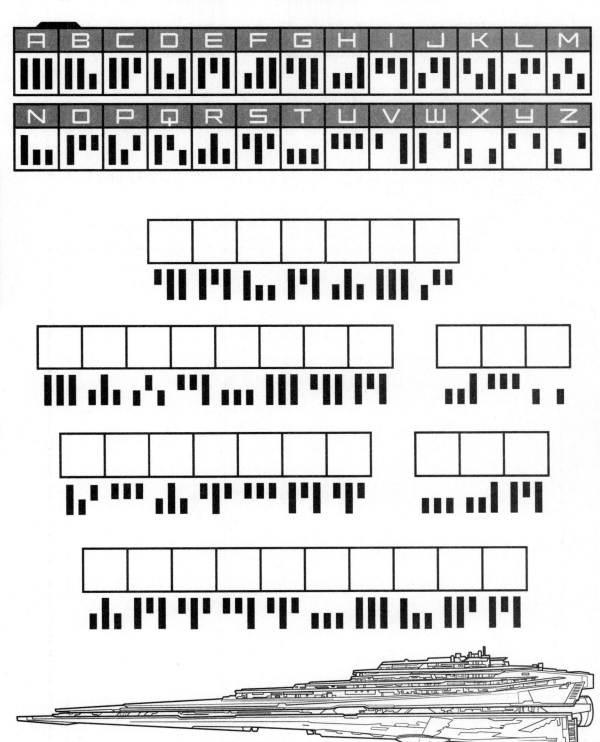

UNSCRAMBLE

Unscramble the letters listed to fit the spaces below.

CONIERETUXE

_ _ _ _ _ _ _ _ _ _ _

SALDUMPEEREER

_ _ _ _ _ _ _ _ _ _ _ _ _

SREEISTANC

_ _ _ _ _ _ _ _ _ _

THISROLD

_ _ _ _ _ _ _ _

SLATBER

_ _ _ _ _ _ _

FOLLOW THE PATH

Using the letters, in order, from the word **TIE FIGHTER**, follow the correct path to find your way through the maze.

START

T	I	E	J	H	T	M	Z
O	S	F	I	G	E	A	S
R	C	E	F	C	R	T	I
O	F	M	A	E	V	U	E
E	I	T	R	F	G	I	F
F	B	C	E	T	H	B	N
I	L	G	F	O	R	S
G	H	U	C	E
M	T	E	R

© LFL

© LFL

SECTOR GRID

Use the grid to help you draw the picture.

Set your
weapons
to stun!

As the Supreme Leader of the First Order, **SNOKE** stands atop an evil regime that mirrors many of the dark traditions of the Galactic Empire. As a striking example, **SNOKE** is flanked by crimson-clad **ELITE PRAETORIAN GUARDS**, loyal protectors encased in ornate armor, ready to defend the Supreme Leader against any threat.

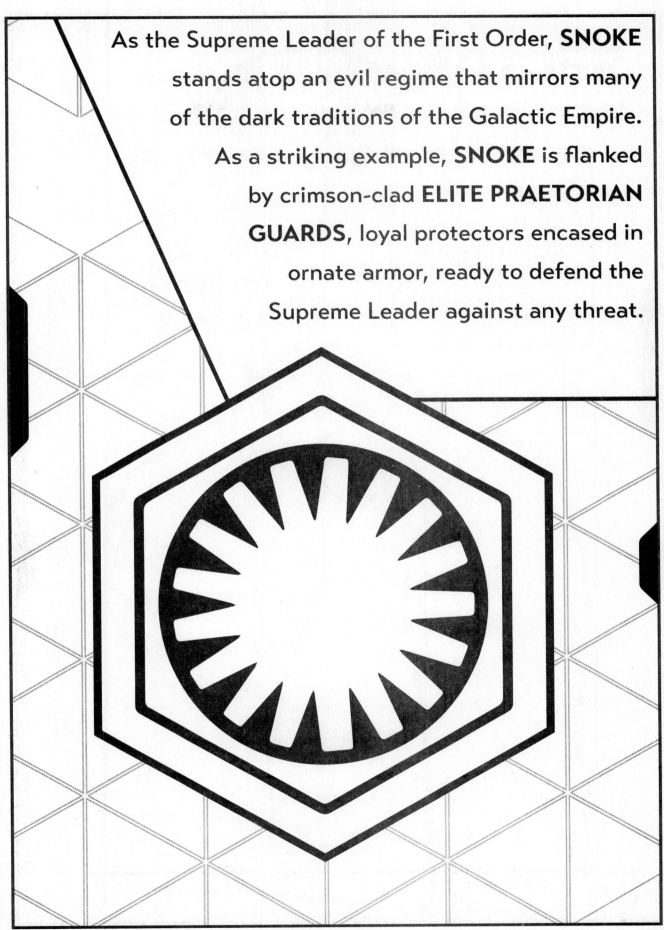

© LFL

SQUARES

Taking turns, connect a line from one symbol to another. Whoever makes the line that completes the box puts their initials inside that box. The person with the most squares at the end of the game wins!

Example

WORD SEARCH

Find the words listed in the puzzle below.

SNOKE	SUPREME
LEADER	FORCE
DROID	TROOPER
GALACTIC	EMPIRE

```
G W G K E Y S A S O L
X K N B R K N W U F V
C S K D I M O E P Z G
Z I T E P T K J R O X
F T T Y M L E D E G H
T E R C E H D K M L Z
Y D C O A P I W E E I
V J R R O L N Q J A O
U M M O O P A F L D Q
S H V B I F E G B E O
B H U L G D Q R V R Z
```

SECRET CODE

Using the secret code decipher the message.

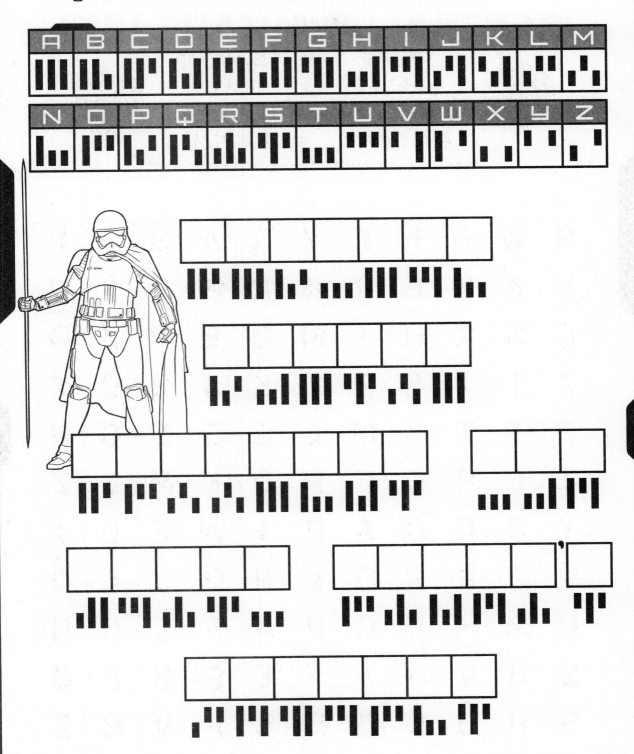

© LFL

HOW MANY WORDS

See how many words you can make from the letters in:

GENERAL ARMITAGE HUX

IMPOSTER

Find the Executioner that is different, that is the imposter.

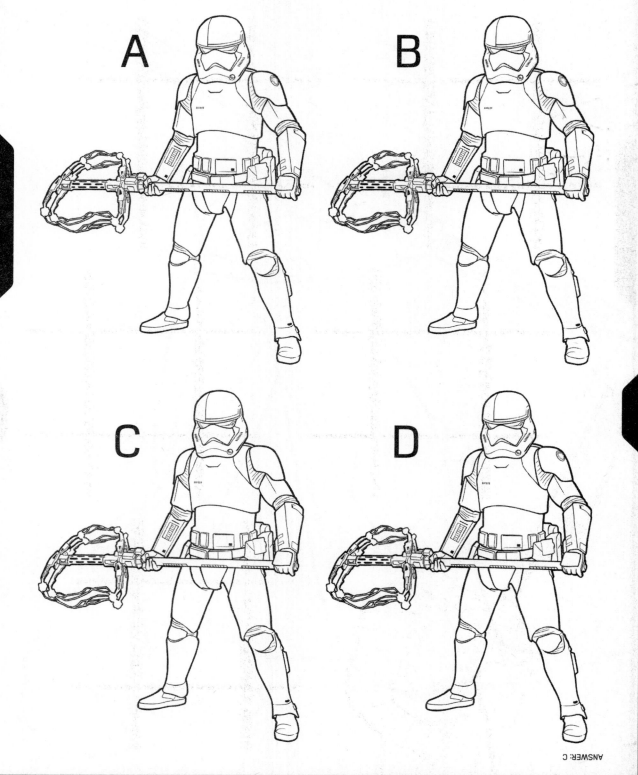

A

B

C

D

TIC-TAC-TOE

Challenge a friend to a game of tic-tac-toe.

MISSING PIECE

Find the square that completes the picture.

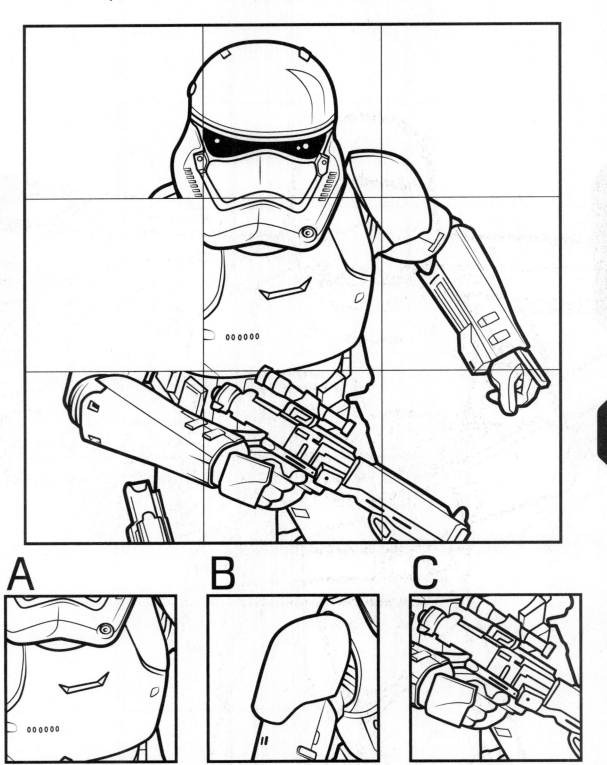

A

B

C

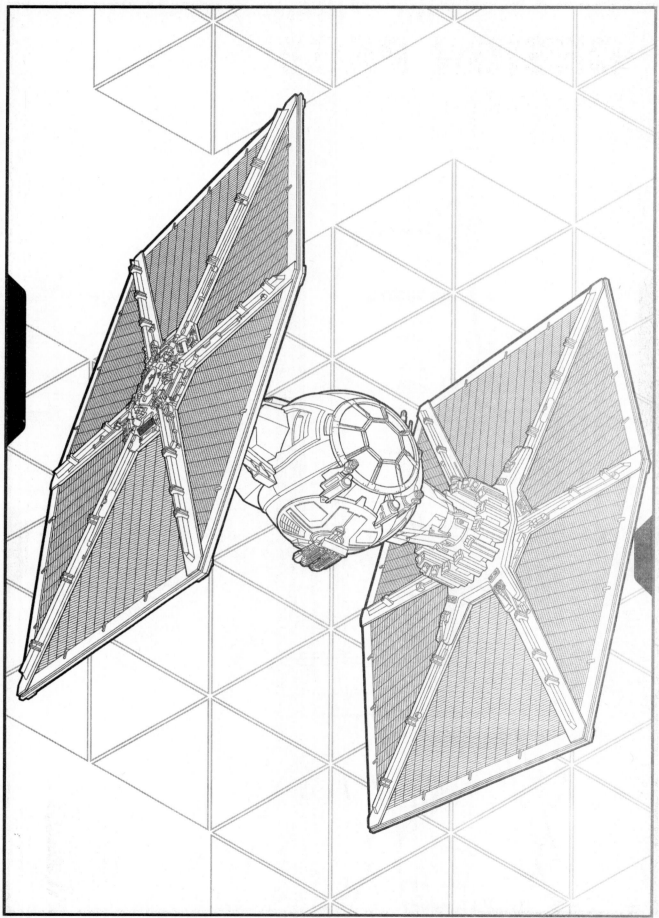

DESIGN PAGE

Design a Knight of Ren.

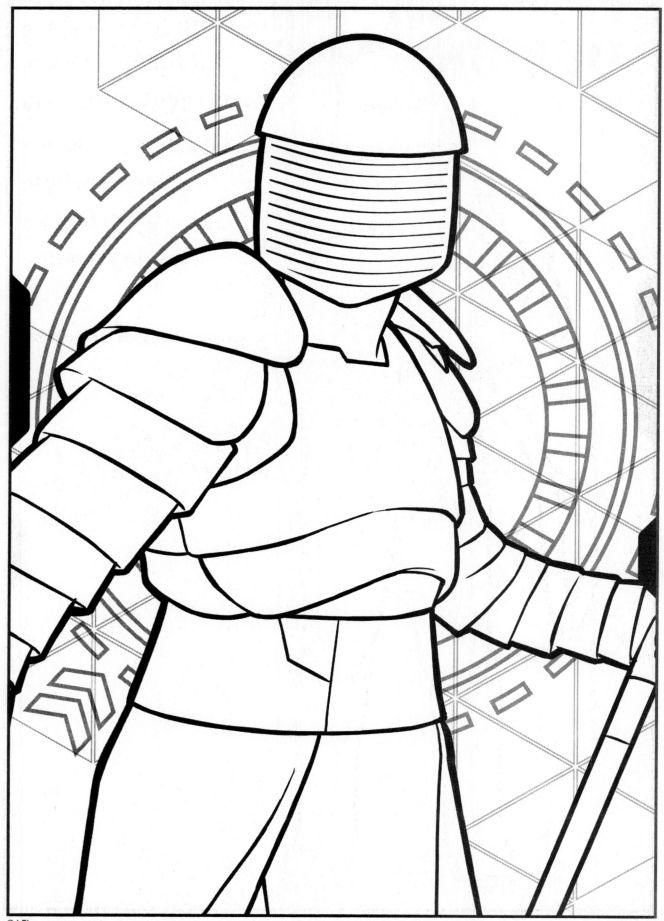

Specialized stormtroopers of the First Order, **FLAMETROOPERS** carry incendiary weapons that can transform any battlefield into a blazing inferno.

IMPOSTER

Find the counterfit TIE Fighter that is different, that is the imposter.

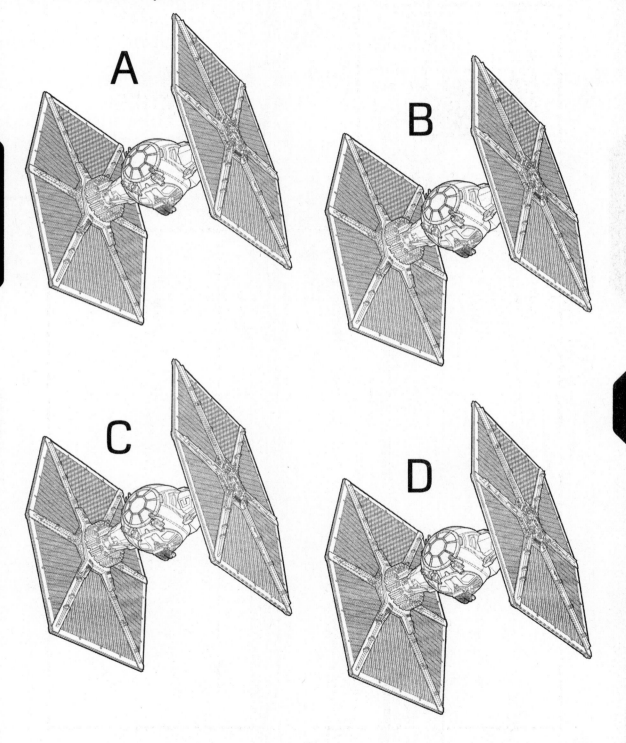

A

B

C

D

SECTOR GRID

Use the grid to help you draw the picture.

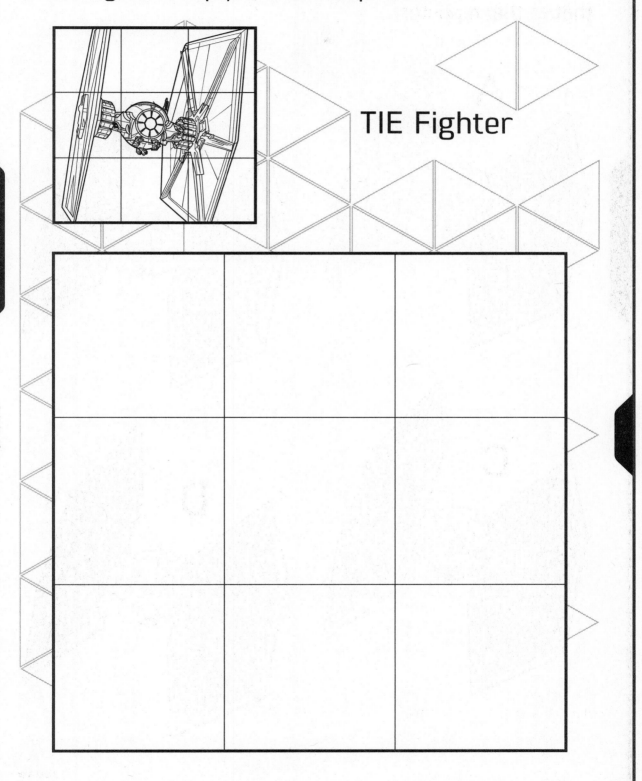

TIE Fighter

FOLLOW THE PATH

Using the letters, in order, from the word **FINALIZER**, follow the correct path to find your way through the maze.

START

F	A	T	E	R	O	M	Z
I	S	H	Z	F	I	N	A
N	A	L	I	C	B	N	L
O	F	M	A	E	V	Z	I
Y	T	N	I	F	R	E	A
T	E	A	P	L	D	B	N
P	F	L	G	F	O	R	S
M	O	I	Z	E	L	C	B
M	O	R	C	R	L	E	W

FINISH

HOW MANY WORDS

See how many words you can make from the letters in:

CAPTAIN PHASMA

MISSING PIECE

Find the square that completes the picture.

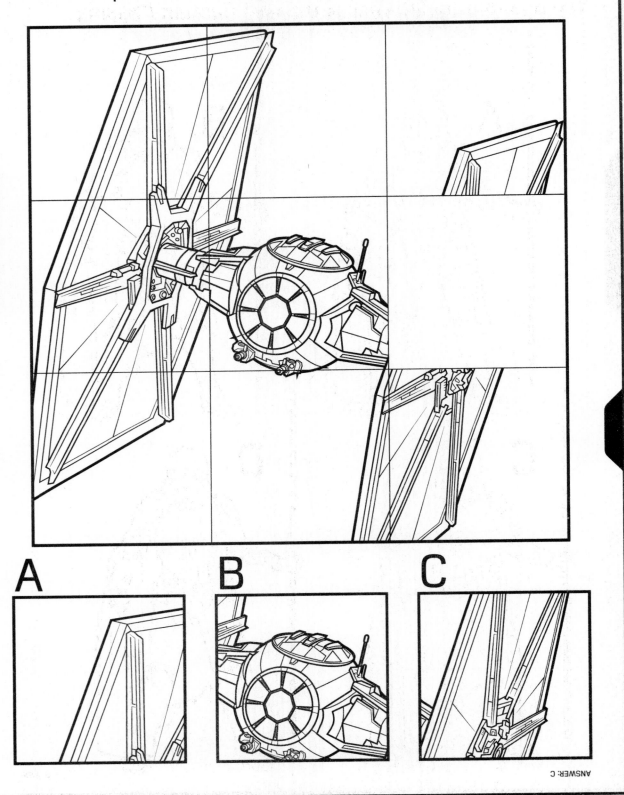

A

B

C

IMPOSTER

Find the Captain Phasma there are three imposters.
The one that is different is the real Captain Phasma.

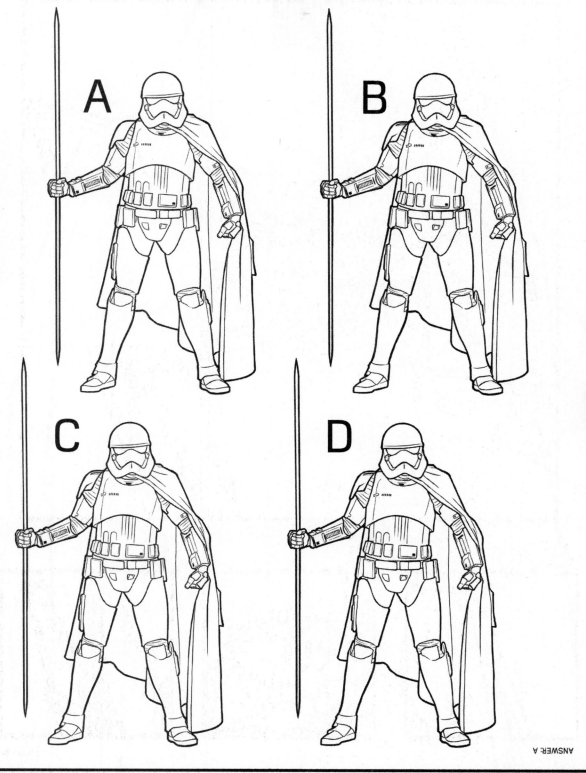

A   B

C   D

DESIGN PAGE

Design your own First Order droid.

SECTOR GRID

Use the grid to help you draw the picture.

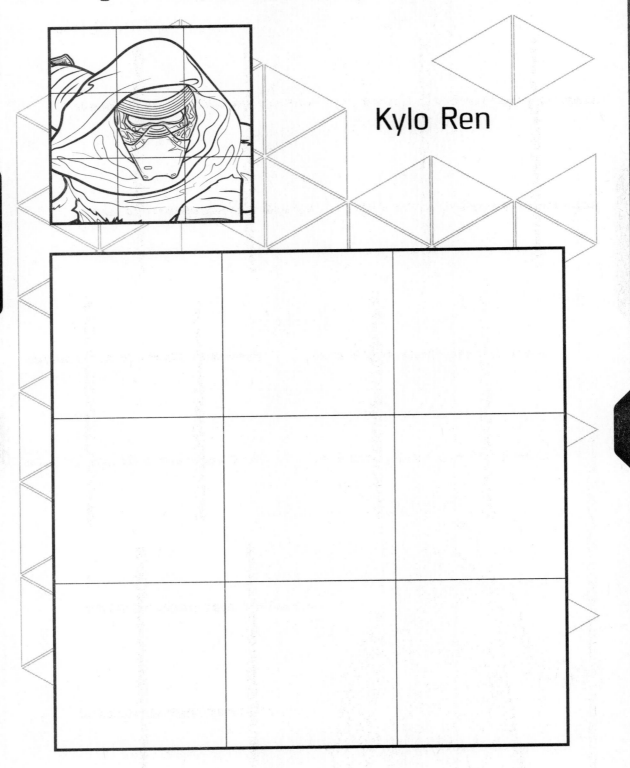

Kylo Ren

TIC-TAC-TOE

Challenge a friend to a game of tic-tac-toe.

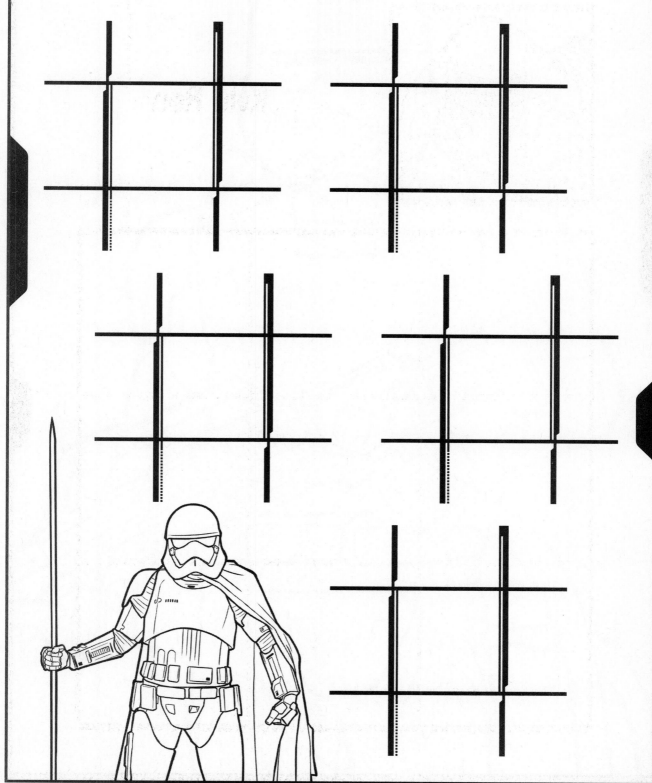

SECRET CODE

Using the secret code decipher the message.

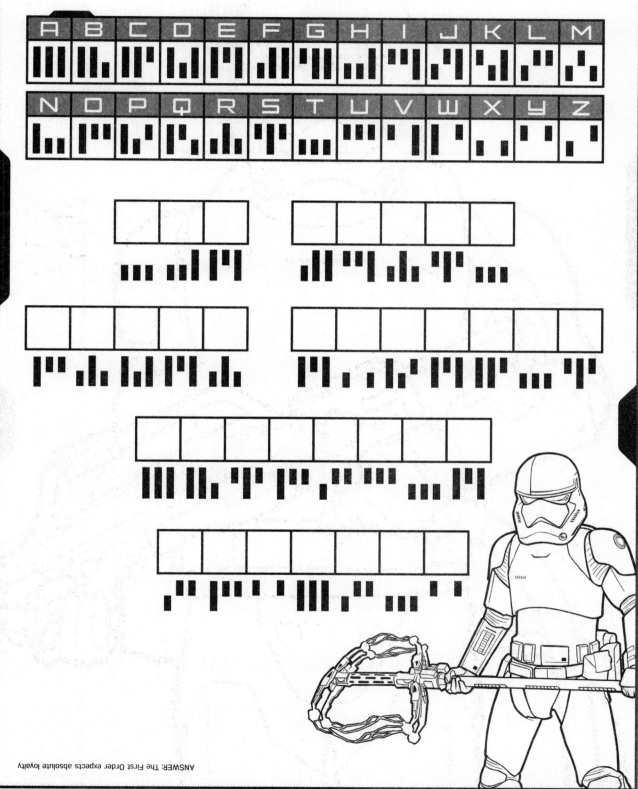

© LFL

WORD SEARCH

Find the words listed in the puzzle below.

ARMATIGE	DESTROYER
WALKER	POWER
SNOKE	SUPREME
LEADER	FORCE

```
T  D  D  E  S  T  R  O  Y  E  R
R  E  K  L  A  W  E  W  B  R  R
D  A  X  S  Z  B  G  Y  V  R  E
J  M  X  N  E  W  I  I  E  J  I
R  I  I  O  P  Z  T  D  W  H  N
Q  R  B  K  W  S  A  J  D  Z  F
H  R  W  E  L  E  M  I  E  E  C
T  N  N  G  L  D  R  Z  C  I  S
O  R  E  W  O  P  A  C  R  G  C
S  U  P  R  E  M  E  W  O  V  K
R  M  E  T  I  V  G  N  F  G  O
```

SQUARES

Taking turns, connect a line from one symbol to another. Whoever makes the line that completes the box puts their initials inside that box. The person with the most squares at the end of the game wins!

Example

UNSCRAMBLE

Unscramble the letters listed to fit the spaces below.

SOTHARCEM

_ _ _ _ _ _ _ _ _

THIERFIGET

_ _ _   _ _ _ _ _ _ _

PHATCASINAMA

_ _ _ _ _ _ _   _ _ _ _ _

KNOES

_ _ _ _ _

AXALGY

_ _ _ _ _ _

FOLLOW THE PATH

Using the letters, in order, from the word **KYLO REN**,
follow the correct path to find your way through the maze.

START

K	Y	L	O	R	O	M	Z
O	S	H	O	E	E	A	S
R	C	E	F	N	K	Y	L
O	F	M	L	Y	V	U	O
N	E	R	O	K	N	E	R
K	Y	L	P	U	D
T	F	O	W	Q	S
B	D	R	N	E	R
M	N	E	C	E	L

FINISH

© LFL

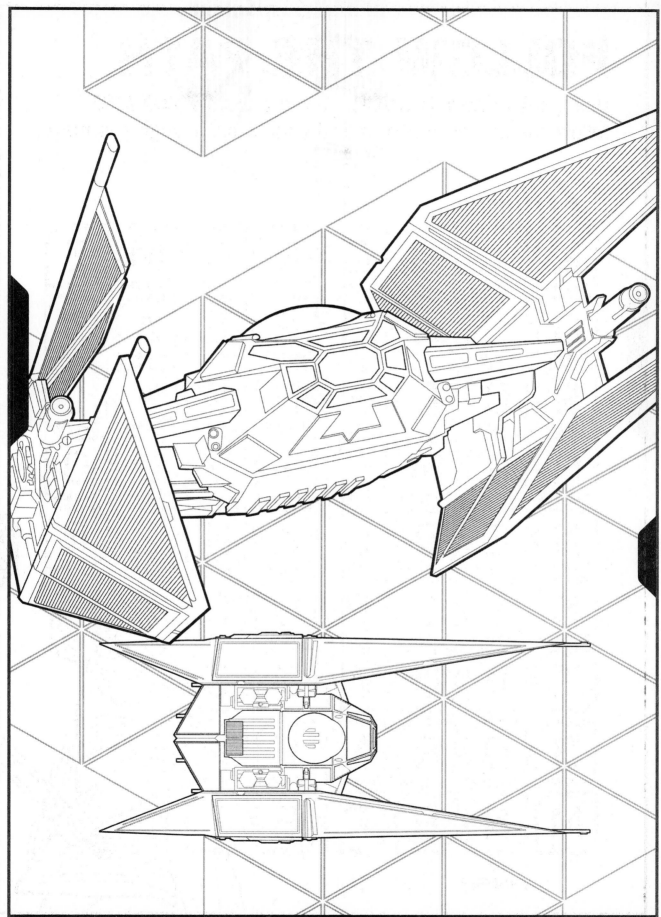

MAZE

Guide the Star Destroyer on patrol of the galaxy.

START

FINISH

TIC-TAC-TOE

Challenge a friend to a game of tic-tac-toe.

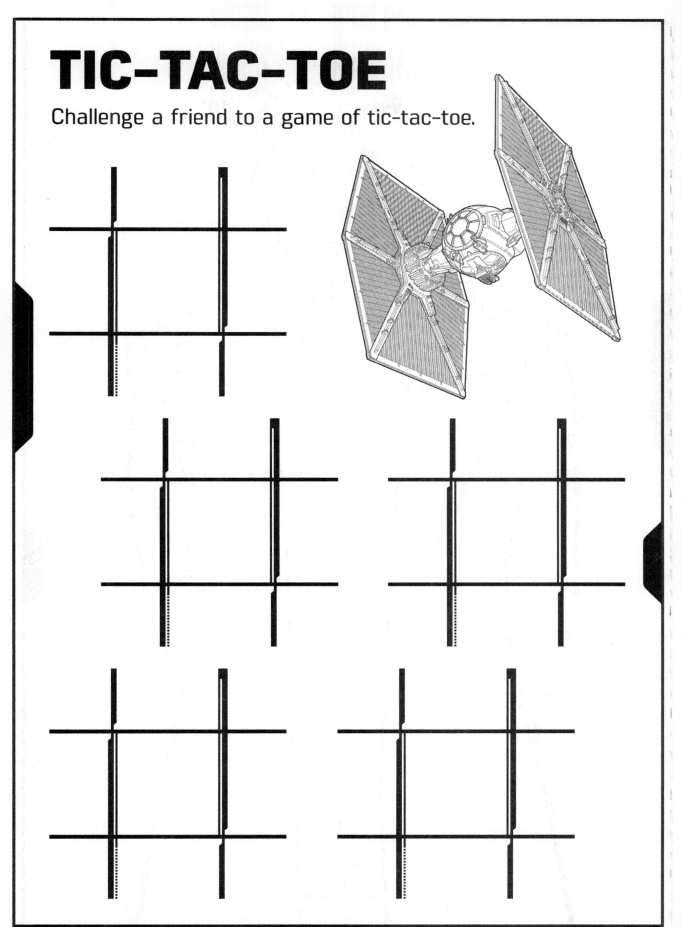

MISSING PIECE

Find the square that completes the picture.

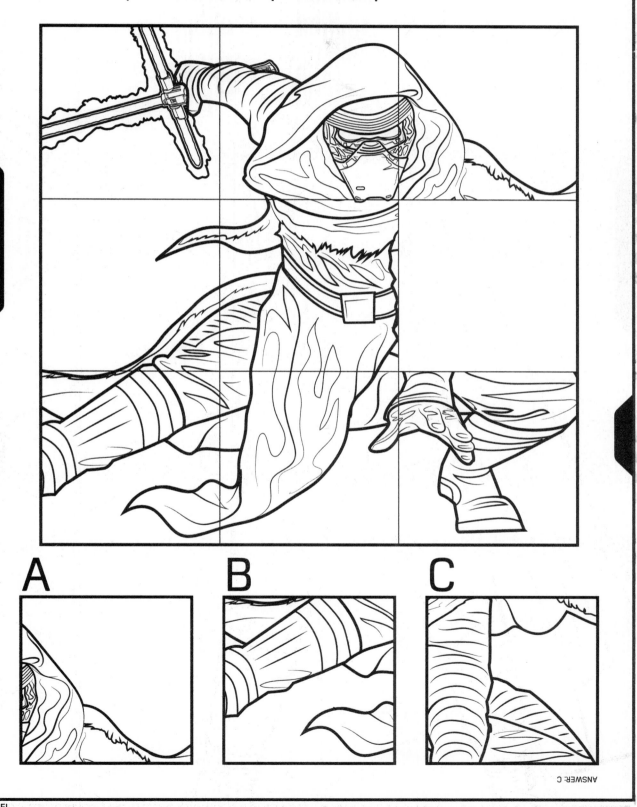

A

B

C

IMPOSTER

Find the First Order BB astromech unit that is different, that is the imposter.

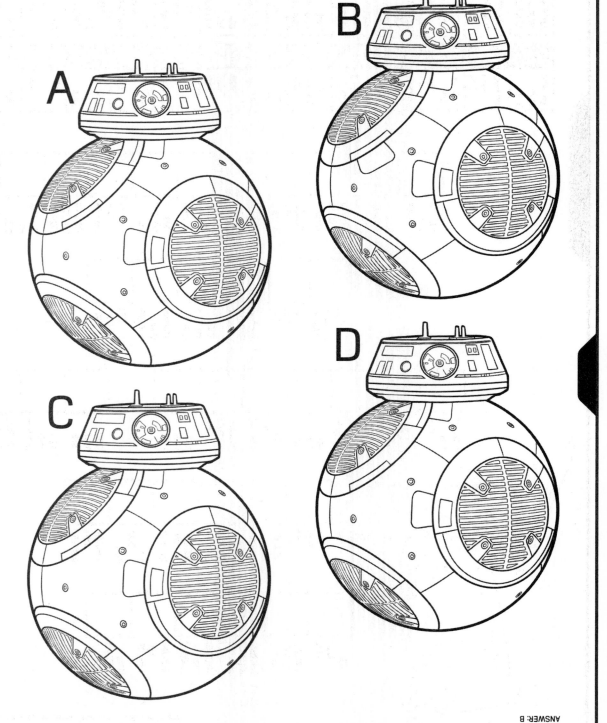

SECRET CODE

Using the secret code decipher the message.

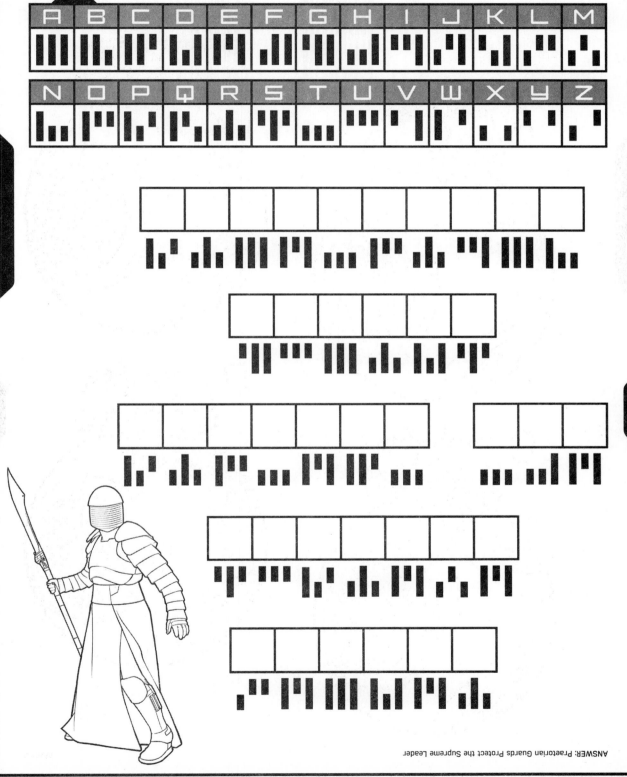

© LFL

SQUARES

Taking turns, connect a line from one symbol to another. Whoever makes the line that completes the box puts their initials inside that box. The person with the most squares at the end of the game wins!

Example

KYLO REN has inherited amazing piloting skills from his father, **HAN SOLO**, though he uses these abilities to pursue the Resistance from the seat of his unique angular **TIE SILENCER.**

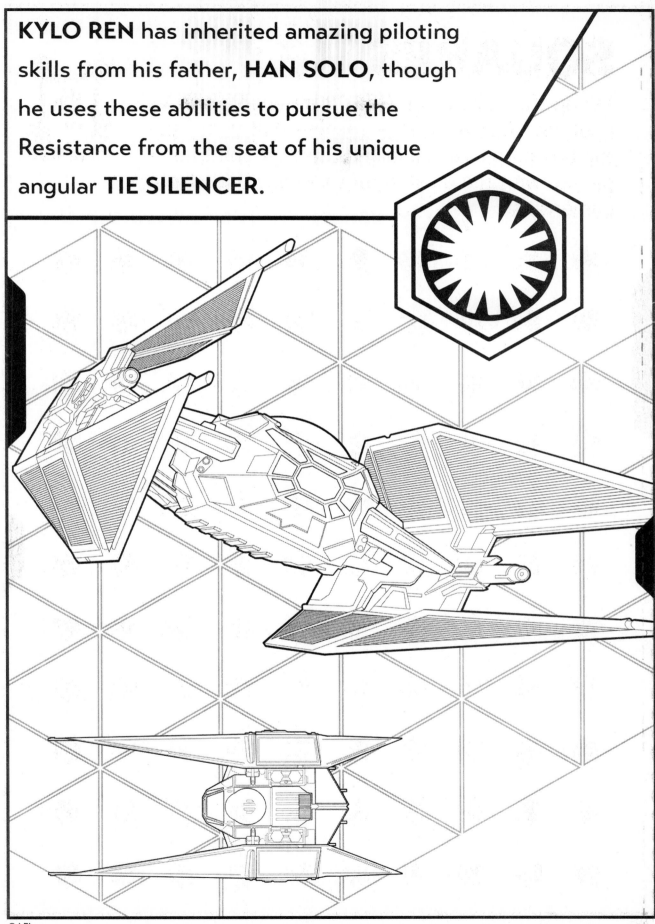

FOLLOW THE PATH

Using the letters, in order, from the word **FIRST ORDER**, follow the correct path to find your way through the maze.

START

F	I	T	I	T	I	R
S	R	H	F	S	T	O	S
T	C	E	R	C	B	R	C
O	R	D	A	E	V	D	I
Y	T	R	O	F	G	E	A
T	E	C	P	I	F	R	N
P	F	L	S	R	O	R	S
M	O	R	T	D	E	C	B
M	O	R	O	R	R	E	W

FINISH

© LFL

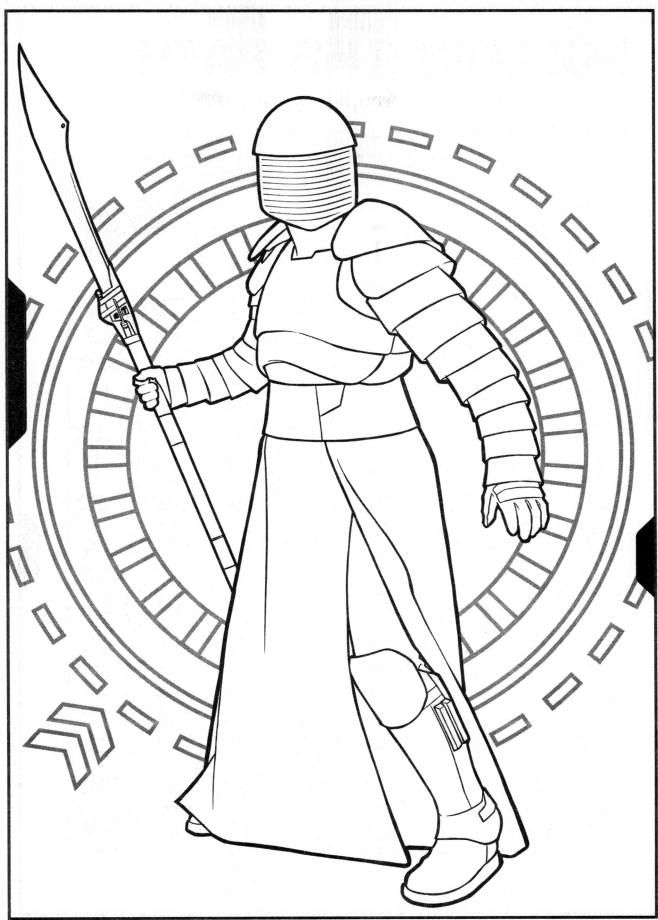

WORD SEARCH

Find the words listed in the puzzle below.

KYLO REN
GALAXY
ARMATIGE
WALKER

GENERAL
DARK SIDE
DESTROYER
POWER

```
M C F L C C L W E S M
X D D K A R A A N D U
B E A E R E R L Z A M
P S N O M W E K P R W
A T O G A O N E N K U
Y R P S T P E R E S A
X O O D I L G K R I B
A Y X P G R J O O D F
L E X K E E T M L E D
A R S A I O X J Y P D
G D E O A X W N K X Q
```

DESIGN PAGE

Design your own Stormtrooper armor.

HOW MANY WORDS

See how many words you can make from the letters in:

KNIGHTS OF REN

SECTOR GRID

Use the grid to help you draw the picture.

General
Armatige Hux

UNSCRAMBLE

Unscramble the letters listed to fit the spaces below.

REYLONK

_ _ _ _   _ _ _

TRADESTORYERS

_ _ _ _ _ _   _ _ _ _ _ _ _

ORMOOTRSTEPR

_ _ _ _ _ _ _ _ _ _ _ _

DADSREIK

_ _ _ _   _ _ _ _

DROTSFIRER

_ _ _ _ _   _ _ _ _ _

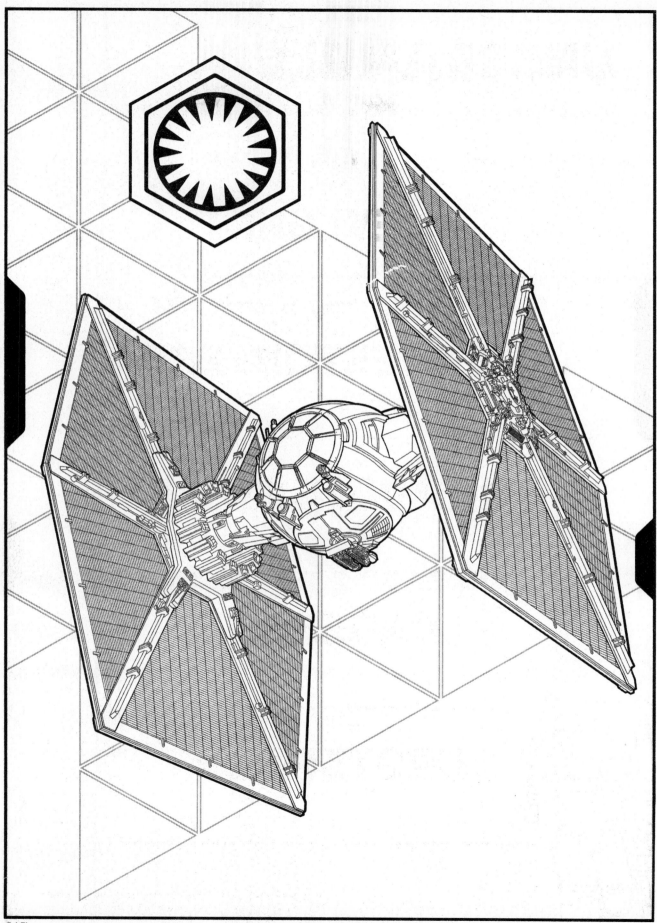

© LFL

The First Order **TIE FIGHTERS** feature improved solar cells, higher-capacity converters, and onboard deflector shields, making these ships far deadlier than the **TIEs** that saw service in the Imperial era.

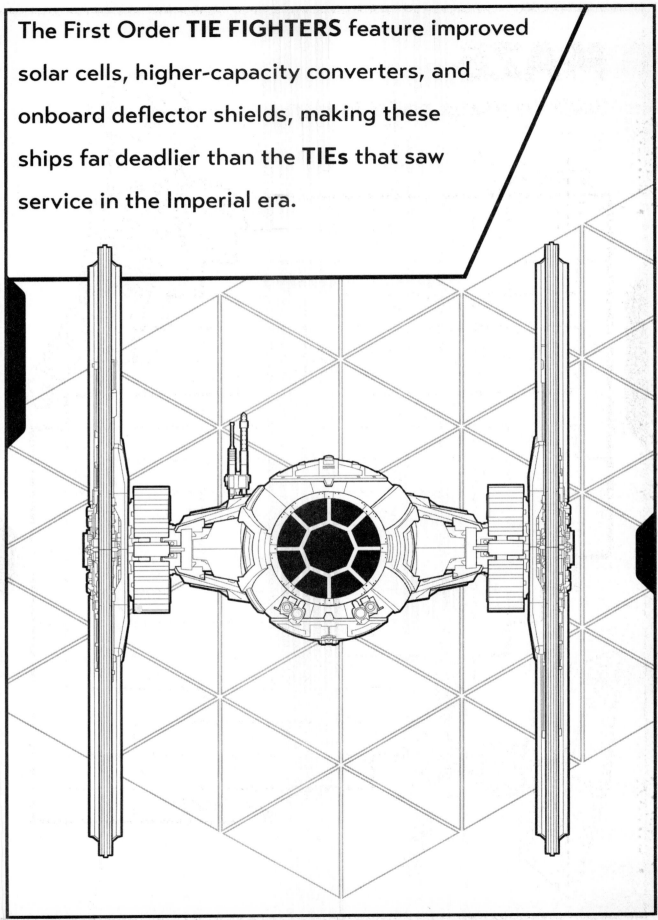

MAZE

Guide the pilot to his TIE Fighter.

START

FINISH

TIC-TAC-TOE

Challenge a friend to a game of tic-tac-toe.

SECTOR GRID

Use the grid to help you draw the picture.

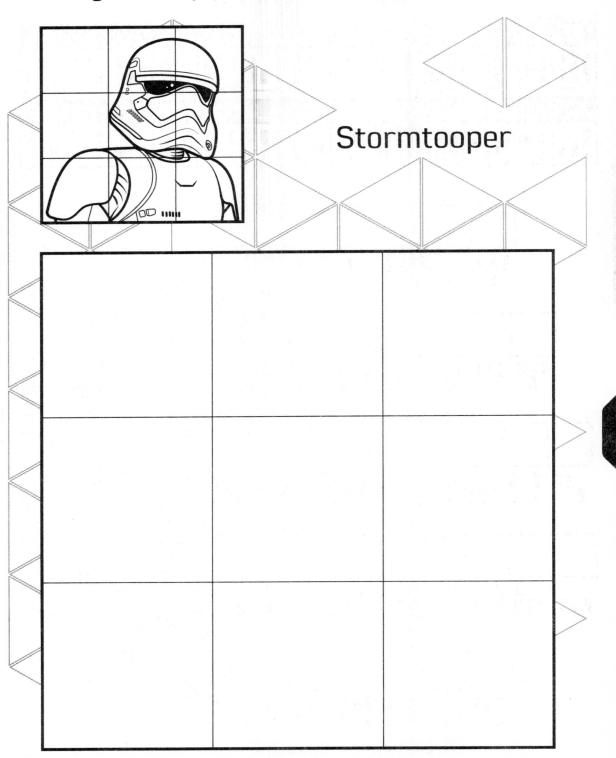

Stormtooper

SECRET CODE

Using the secret code decipher the message.

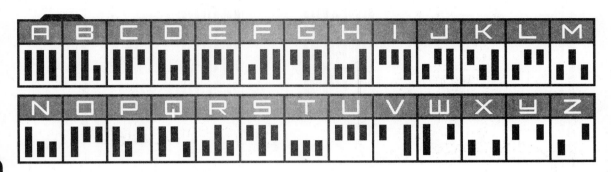

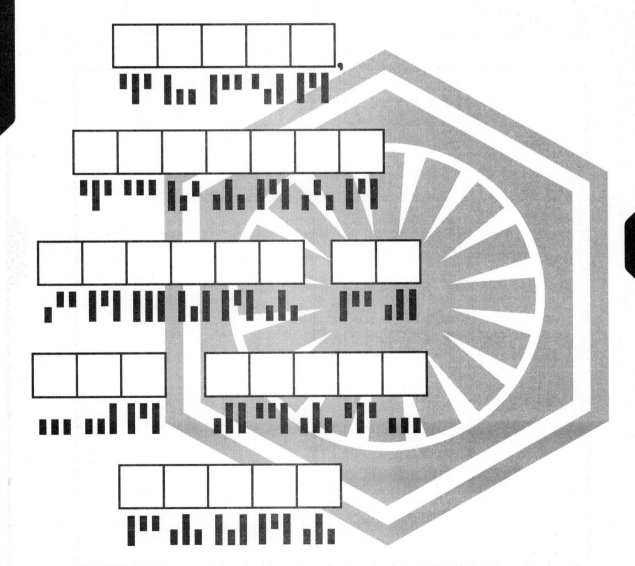

© LFL

Clad in distinctive metallic armor, **CAPTAIN PHASMA** commands the First Order's legions of troopers. Having survived the destruction of Starkiller base, she has a personal score to settle with the Resistance.

FOLLOW THE PATH

Using the letters, in order, from the word **DARKSIDE**, follow the correct path to find your way through the maze.

START

D	A	R	K	K	O	M	Z
O	D	I	S	R	E	A	S
M	E	E	F	C	B	N	C
A	D	M	A	E	R	K	S
R	T	D	E	D	A	H	I
K	S	I	P	L	P	E	D
P	F	L	G	F	A	D	S
M	O	R	C	K	R	C	B
M	O	R	C	S	I	D	E

FINISH

HOW MANY WORDS

See how many words you can make from the letters in:

THE FIRST ORDER

SQUARES

Taking turns, connect a line from one symbol to another. Whoever makes the line that completes the box puts their initials inside that box. The person with the most squares at the end of the game wins!

Example

Though Starkiller base has been destroyed, **GENERAL ARMITAGE HUX'S** command to fire the devastating weapon eradicated the New Republic in a single strike. From the bridge of the First Order's Star Destroyer *Finalizer*, **HUX** continues to pursue the destruction of the Resistance.

WORD SEARCH

Find the words listed in the puzzle below.

BLASTER	TIE FIGHTER
FIRST	ORDER
KYLO REN	GENERAL
GALAXY	DARKSIDE

```
Q B G K L A R E N E G
N R I E F D S U Q I D
B R E V M Q R I H A L
W L U T K Y L O R E N
J C A O H O I K H M Y
R A T S K G S H J S L
D A D X T I I X L M X
A L W O D E U F G K K
M D W E O P R N E G A
C D Z G A L A X Y I C
R E D R O T S R I F T
```

The First Order benefits from the latest in technology across all its activities. This includes dark, gleaming **BB ASTROMECH UNITS** of its own that keep the starships and machinery operational.

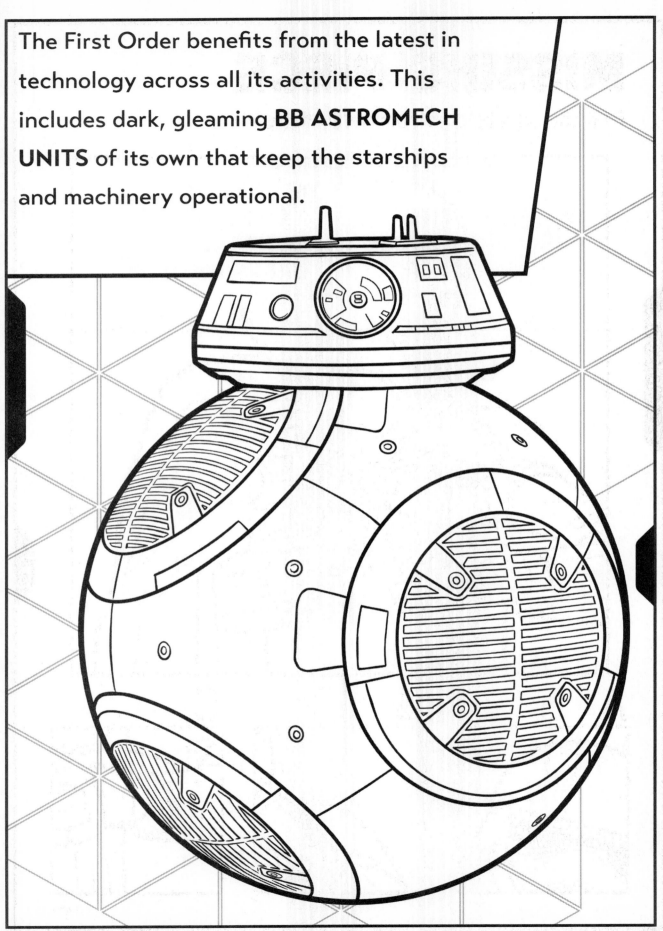

MISSING PIECE

Find the square that completes the picture.

A

B

C

ANSWER: A

DESIGN PAGE

Design your own First Order TIE Fighter.

IMPOSTER

Find the Elite Praetorian Guard that is different, that is the imposter.

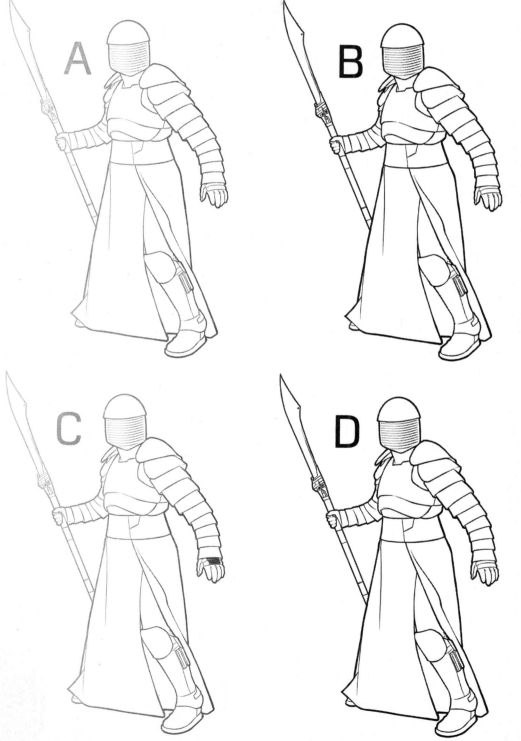

ANSWER: C

SECRET CODE

Using the secret code decipher the message.

© LFL

Though his powers in the dark side have increased, **KYLO** still has much to prove to his mentor and the shadowy commander of the First Order, **SUPREME LEADER SNOKE.**

TIC-TAC-TOE

Challenge a friend to a game of tic-tac-toe.

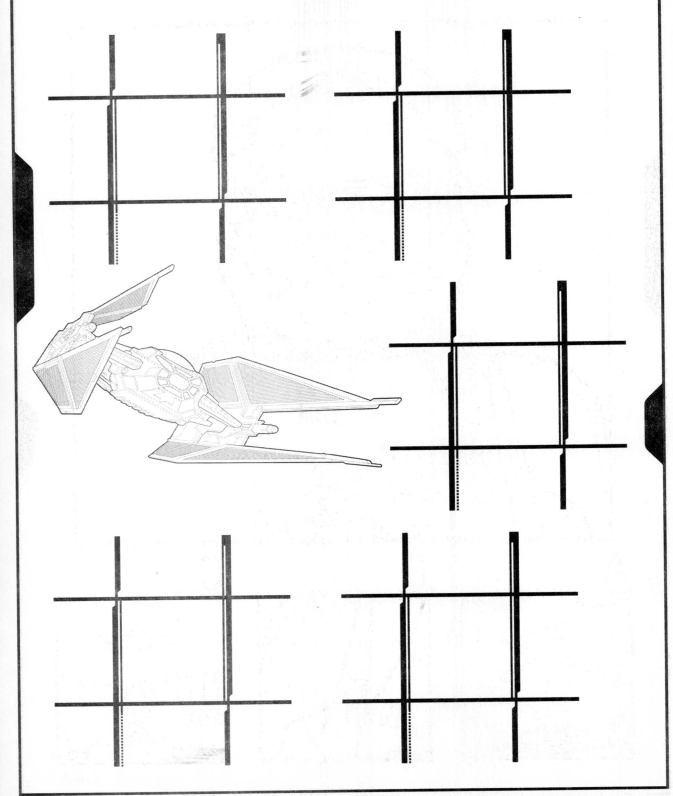

MISSING PIECE

Find the square that completes the picture.

A

B

C

SECTOR GRID

Use the grid to help you draw the picture.

Captain
Phasma

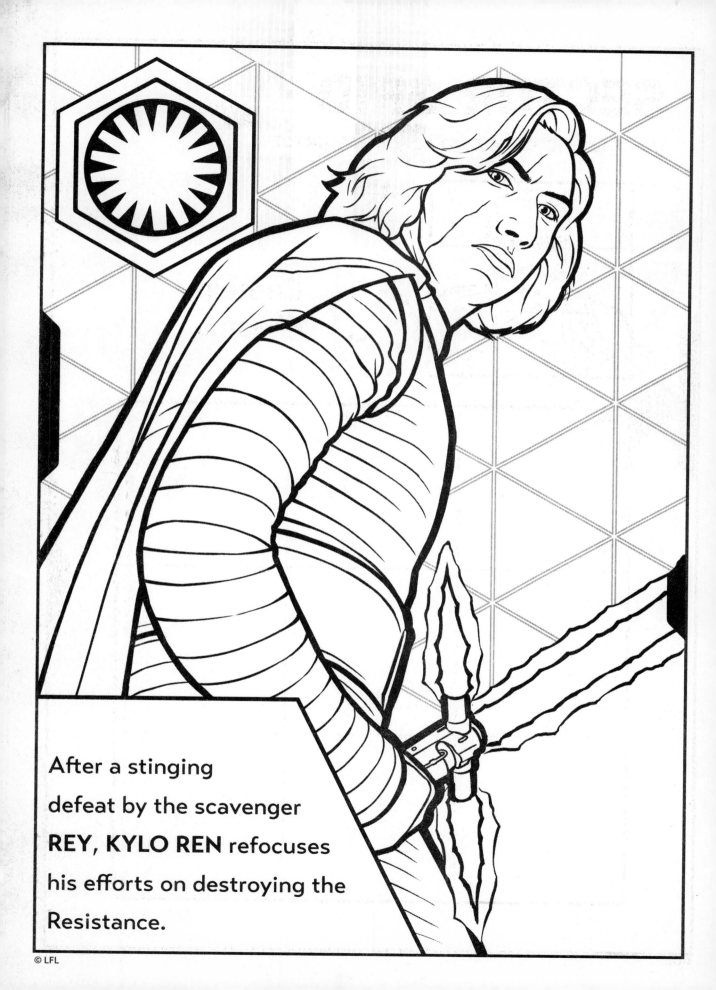

After a stinging defeat by the scavenger **REY, KYLO REN** refocuses his efforts on destroying the Resistance.

STAR WARS ™

COLORING AND ACTIVITY BOOK
WITH STICKERS

starwars.com

© & ™ Lucasfilm Ltd.